P9-EME-955

STORY POEMS NEW AND OLD

Also by William Cole

HUMOROUS POETRY FOR CHILDREN

STORY POEMS
New and Old

edited by

WILLIAM COLE

Illustrated by Walter Buehr

THE WORLD PUBLISHING COMPANY

CLEVELAND AND NEW YORK

Published by THE WORLD PUBLISHING COMPANY
2231 WEST 110TH STREET, CLEVELAND 2, OHIO

Published simultaneously in Canada by
NELSON, FOSTER & SCOTT LTD.

Library of Congress Catalog Card Number: 57-5897

COPYRIGHT ACKNOWLEDGMENTS

The editor and The World Publishing Company herewith render thanks to the following authors, publishers, and agents whose interest, co-operation, and permission to reprint have made possible the preparation of *Story Poems New and Old*. All possible care has been taken to trace the ownership of every selection included and to make full acknowledgment for its use. If any errors have accidentally occurred, they will be corrected in subsequent editions, provided notification is sent to the publisher.

Brandt & Brandt, for "The Mountain Whippoorwill" from *Selected Works*, by Stephen Vincent Benét, published by Rinehart & Company, copyright, 1922, Stephen Vincent Benét, copyright renewed, 1950, Rosemary Carr Benét; for "The Powerful Eyes o' Jeremy Tait" from *Random Rhymes and Odd Numbers*, by Wallace Irwin, published by The Macmillan Company, copyright, 1906, Wallace Irwin; for "The Ballad of the Harp-weaver" from *Collected Poems*, by Edna St. Vincent Millay, published by Harper & Brothers, copyright 1922, 1950, Edna St. Vincent Millay. Reprinted by permission of Brandt & Brandt.

Jonathan Cape Limited and Mrs. H. M. Davies, for "Sheep" from *Collected Poems*, by W. H. Davies, published by Jonathan Cape Limited.

Chapman & Grimes, Inc., for "The Glory Trail" from *Sun and Saddle Leather*, by Badger Clark, published by Richard C. Badger, copyright, 1942, Chapman & Grimes, Inc.

Coward-McCann, Inc., for "A Lady Comes to an Inn" from *The Creaking Stair*, by Elizabeth Coatsworth, copyright, 1949, Coward-McCann, Inc.

The Cresset Press, for "The Princess and the Gypsies" from *Collected Poems*, by Frances Cornford, copyright, 1954.

Dodd, Mead & Company, Inc., for "Blow Me Eyes!" and "A Nautical Extravaganza" from *Nautical Lays of a Landsman*, by Wallace Irwin, reprinted by permission of Dodd, Mead & Company, Inc.; for "The Cremation of Sam McGee" from *Complete Poems*, by Robert W. Service, reprinted by permission of Dodd, Mead & Company, Inc. and the Ryerson Press.

Doubleday & Company, Inc., for "The Green Fiddler" from *Taxis and Toadstools*, by Rachel Field, copyright, 1926, Doubleday & Company, Inc.; for "small talk" and "the flattered lightning bug" from *The Lives and Times of Archy and Mehitabel*, by Don Marquis, copyright, 1927, Doubleday & Company, Inc.

E. P. Dutton & Co., Inc., for "The Dog's Cold Nose" from *Lyric Laughter*, by Arthur Guiterman, copyright, 1939, E. P. Dutton & Co., Inc. Reprinted by permission of E. P. Dutton & Co., Inc.

Henry Holt and Company, Inc., for "Off the Ground" from *Collected Poems*, Volume II, by Walter de la Mare, copyright, 1920, Henry Holt and Company, Inc., copyright, 1948, Walter de la Mare; for "Brown's

CONTENTS

INTRODUCTION   15

BELLOC, HILAIRE   *Matilda*   21
(1870-1953)

BENÉT, STEPHEN VINCENT   *The Mountain Whip-*
(1898-1943)   *poorwill*   23

BENÉT, WILLIAM ROSE   *Jesse James*   29
(1886-1950)

BUCHANAN, ROBERT   *The Green Gnome*   33
(1841-1901)

BUNNER, H. C.   *Grandfather Watts's*
(1855-1896)   *Private Fourth*   35

CARRYL, GUY WETMORE   *The Arrogant Frog and*
(1873-1904)   *the Superior Bull*   37
   The Embarrassing Epi-
   sode of Little Miss
   Muffet   38

CLARK, BADGER   *The Glory Trail*   40
(1883-   )

COATSWORTH, ELIZA-   *A Lady Comes to an Inn*   42
BETH J. (1893-   )

CORNFORD, FRANCES   *The Princess and the*
(1886-1960)   *Gypsies*   43

DAVIES, W. H.   *Sheep*   45
(1871-1940)

DE LA MARE, WALTER   *Off the Ground*   46
(1873-1956)

FARJEON, ELEANOR AND   *Henry VIII*   50
HERBERT (1881-)
(1887-1945)

FIELD, EUGENE   *The Death of Robin*
(1850-1895)   *Hood*   51
   Song of the All-wool
   Shirt   53
FIELD, RACHEL   *The Green Fiddler*   54
(1894-1942)

FIELDS, JAMES THOMAS   *The Owl-critic*   56
(1817-1881)

FLECKER, JAMES ELROY   *Lord Arnaldos*   59
(1884-1915)

FROST, ROBERT   *Brown's Descent*   60
(1875-1963)

GARNETT, RICHARD   *The Highwayman's*
(1835-1906)   *Ghost*   63

GARSTIN, CROSBIE   *The Figure-head*   64
(1887-1930)

GIBSON, W. W.   *Flannan Isle*   66
(1878-1962)

GILBERT, W. S.   *There Lived a King*   70
(1836-1911)   *The Perils of Invisi-*
   bility   71

GILLILAN, S. W.   *Finnigin to Flannigan*   75
(1869-1954)

GUITERMAN, ARTHUR   *The Dog's Cold Nose*   76
(1871-1943)

HARTE, BRET   *The Spelling Bee at*
(1836-1902)   *Angels*   78

HERFORD, OLIVER   *The Fall of J. W. Beane*   82
(1863-1935)

HOLMES, OLIVER WEN-   *The Deacon's Master-*
DELL (1809-1894)   *piece*   86

HOOD, THOMAS   *The Dream of Eugene*
(1799-1845)   *Aram*   91

IRWIN, WALLACE   *Blow Me Eyes!*   98
(1876-1959)   *A Nautical Extrava-*
               ganza   100
               The Powerful Eyes o'
               Jeremy Tait   102

KEATS, JOHN   *La Belle Dame Sans*
(1795-1821)   *Merci*   105

KELLER, MARTHA   *Brady's Bend*   107
(1902-   )

KINGSLEY, CHARLES   *The Knight's Leap*   110
(1819-1875)

LELAND, CHARLES GOD- *The Story of Samuel*
FREY (1824-1903)   *Jackson*   112

LEWIS, M. A.   *The Caulker*   115
(1890-   )

LINDSAY, VACHEL   *The Blacksmith's Sere-*
(1879-1931)   *nade*   118

LONGFELLOW, HENRY   *The Luck of Edenhall* 120
WADSWORTH   *Paul Revere's Ride*   122
(1807-1882)

LOVER, SAMUEL   *Paddy O'Rafther*   128
(1797-1868)

LOWELL, ROBERT   The Relief of Lucknow   129
    (1816-1891)

MARQUIS, DON   small talk   133
    (1878-1937)   the flattered lightning
                                  bug   134

MARRYAT, FREDERICK   The Old Navy   135
    (1792-1848)

MASEFIELD, JOHN   Cape Horn Gospel—I   137
    (1878-   )   The Yarn of the Loch
                                  Achray   138

MILLAY, EDNA ST. VIN-   The Ballad of the Harp-
    CENT (1892-1950)   weaver   140

NASH, OGDEN   The Boy Who Laughed
    (1902-   )   at Santa Claus   146

NOYES, ALFRED   Forty Singing Seamen   148
    (1880-1958)

PEACOCK, THOMAS LOVE   The Priest and the Mul-
    (1785-1866)   berry Tree   154
                             The War-song of Dinas
                                  Vawr   155

POE, EDGAR ALLAN   Annabel Lee   156
    (1809-1849)

RICHARDS, LAURA E.   A Legend of Lake Okee-
    (1850-1943)   finokee   158

RILEY, JAMES WHITCOMB   The Old Man and Jim   160
    (1849-1916)

ROBINSON, EDWIN   Richard Cory   162
    ARLINGTON
    (1869-1935)

SAXE, JOHN GODFREY   The Blind Men and the
(1816-1887)   Elephant   163

                            The Youth and the
                              Northwind   165

SCOTT, SIR WALTER   Allen-a-Dale   170
(1771-1832)   Lochinvar   171

SERVICE, ROBERT W.   The Cremation of Sam
(1874-1958)   McGee   173

SHORTER, DORA SIGERSON   Ballad of the Little
(1866-1918)   Black Hound   178

SOUTHEY, ROBERT   Bishop Hatto   183
(1774-1843)

STEVENSON, ROBERT LOUIS   Christmas at Sea   187
(1850-1894)

SWIFT, JONATHAN   Baucis and Philemon   189
(1667-1745)

TAYLOR, BAYARD   The Three Songs   193
(1825-1878)

TENNYSON, ALFRED LORD   Lady Clare   194
(1809-1892)

THAYER, ERNEST LAW-   Casey at the Bat   197
RENCE (1863-1940)

THOMPSON, LULU E.   In Hardin County, 1809   200
(1839-1916)

WALKER, MARGARET   Molly Means   202
(1915-   )

WALLER, JOHN FRANCIS   The Spinning Wheel   204
(1810-1894)

WHITTIER, JOHN GREEN-   *Skipper Ireson's Ride*   205
   LEAF (1809-1892)

WOOLSON, CONSTANCE   *Kentucky Belle*   209
   FENIMORE (1840-1894)

UNKNOWN   *Abdullah Bulbul Amir*   216
   Because I Were Shy   219
   The Eddystone Light   220
   The Fox   221
   Get Up and Bar the Door   222
   Green Broom   224
   How Robin Hood
   Rescued the Widow's
   Sons   225
   Kitty of Coleraine   230
   A Longford Legend   231
   May Colvin   232
   Old Wichet   235
   The Sad Tale of Mr.
   Mears   237
   The Snuff-boxes   238
   There Was an Old
   Woman   238
   True Thomas   239
   The Twa Corbies   242
   Waltzing Matilda   243
   The Zebra Dun   246

TITLE INDEX   249

INDEX OF FIRST LINES   253

To Mother, with love

INTRODUCTION

INTRODUCTIONS to books of poetry for young people always say these three things: (1) poetry is important in your life; (2) not enough people read poetry; (3) the poetry you read when you're young will lead you to read more and better poetry when you're older. All these things are true; in fact they're so true that I hope they'll be printed in the front of every collection of poetry for young people ever published.

The world's first poets were the storytellers. Long before man could write, and thousands of years before there were books, the hunters would gather around the fire after dark and the storyteller would tell them of the adventures of the day or recount legends of their ancestors. These earliest stories were sung or chanted rhythmically. And later on there were the folk ballads and the songs of the troubadours, who were paid to sing fine stories, usually exaggerated, about the heroism and virtues of their lords and masters. Many of those early ballads were grand stories; they were passed down from generation to generation, and we still hear them sung by the folk singers today and find them in books—there are a few in this one.

As with anything else, there is art in the telling or writing of a good story in verse. A story poem points up the dramatic parts of a tale; the poet doesn't have time to fool around with setting the stage or describing the characters down to the last eyelash. He wants to tell a neat and complete and exciting (or funny) story in a way that keeps you bounding along with him, and in a way which gives you the feeling that you're there, right in the middle of the story that is unfolding. These, more than most poems, are fun to read aloud. Most of them have a rhythm, a regular meter, that sounds fine. Some of them are very dramatic; exciting things happen, and they should be read aloud with a great deal of hip-hip-hooray, in a let-yourself-go manner.

Some of the poetry in this book—well, let's be honest—most of the poetry in this book isn't great poetry. A story poem isn't personal; it doesn't bring out the intensity of feeling from the poet that a great poem does. He's telling a tale, and he's got to keep himself out of it and keep his eye on the narrative. But some of the tales *are* great stories.

You will find that many well-known story poems have been left out of this book. This isn't because they're not good poems or because I couldn't find them. Quite the reverse—it's impossible to escape them, they appear in so many books. I particularly mean poems like *The Highwayman* and *The Pied Piper of Hamelin* and *Gunga Din.* Each of these is in at least twenty other collections for young people, and I didn't want to take up space for the old and familiar when I could use it for the new and unfamiliar. If you read poetry at all, you'll certainly come across them. I've included a *few* of the well-knowns—the ones I like the best, such as *The Deacon's Masterpiece* and *Lochinvar.*

If there are poems in this book that you particularly like, I wish you'd do what I did when I was first reading poetry: write the author's name down and the next time you're in a library—which will be very soon, I hope—look for his books or comb the index of the biggest anthology you can find, looking for him. To discover a good poet who is new to you is just like making a new friend, a friend who will be with you for life.

I would like to quote to you something said by a fine English poet, C. Day Lewis, in his book *Poetry for You*: ". . . to learn poetry is to learn a respect for words; and without this respect for words, you will never be able to think clearly or express yourself properly: and until you can do that, you'll never fully grow up—not though you live to be a hundred."

Finally, let me make a deep bow of thanks to my editor, Velma V. Varner, for all the hard work and helpful hints she contributed while this book was being assembled.

WILLIAM COLE

STORY POEMS NEW AND OLD

MATILDA

who told lies, and was burned to death

Matilda told such Dreadful Lies,
It made one Gasp and Stretch one's Eyes;
Her Aunt, who from her Earliest Youth,
Had kept a Strict Regard for Truth,
Attempted to Believe Matilda:
The effort very nearly killed her,
And would have done so, had not She
Discovered this Infirmity.
For once, towards the Close of Day,
Matilda, growing tired of play,
And finding she was left alone,
Went tiptoe to the Telephone
And summoned the Immediate Aid
Of London's Noble Fire-Brigade.
Within an hour the Gallant Band
Were pouring in on every hand,
From Putney, Hackney Downs and Bow.

With Courage high and Hearts a-glow,
They galloped, roaring through the Town,
"Matilda's House is Burning Down!"
Inspired by British Cheers and Loud
Proceeding from the Frenzied Crowd,
They ran their ladders through a score
Of windows on the Ball Room Floor;
And took Peculiar Pains to Souse
The Pictures up and down the House,
Until Matilda's Aunt succeeded
In showing them they were not needed;
And even then she had to pay
To get the Men to go away!

It happened that a few Weeks later
Her Aunt was off to the Theatre
To see that Interesting Play
The Second Mrs. Tanqueray.
She had refused to take her Niece
To hear that Entertaining Piece:
A Deprivation Just and Wise
To Punish her for Telling Lies.
That Night a Fire DID break out—
You should have heard Matilda Shout!
You should have heard her Scream and Bawl,
And throw the window up and call
To People passing in the Street—
(The rapidly increasing Heat
Encouraging her to obtain
Their confidence)—but all in vain!
For every time She shouted "Fire!"
They only answered "Little Liar!"
And therefore when her Aunt returned,
Matilda, and the House, were Burned.

Hilaire Belloc

THE MOUNTAIN WHIPPOORWILL

or, How Hill-Billy Jim Won the Great Fiddlers' Prize

(A Georgia Romance)

Up in the mountains, it's lonesome all the time,
(Sof' win' slewin' thu' the sweet-potato vine).

Up in the mountains, it's lonesome for a child,
(Whippoorwills a-callin' when the sap runs wild).

Up in the mountains, mountains in the fog,
Everythin's as lazy as an old houn' dog.

Born in the mountains, never raised a pet,
Don't want nuthin' an' never got it yet.

Born in the mountains, lonesome-born,
Raised runnin' ragged thu' the cockleburrs and corn.

Never knew my pappy, mebbe never should.
Think he was a fiddle made of mountain laurel-wood.

Never had a mammy to teach me pretty-please.
Think she was a whippoorwill, a-skitin' thu' the trees.

Never had a brother ner a whole pair of pants,
But when I start to fiddle, why, yuh got to start to dance!

Listen to my fiddle—Kingdom Come—Kingdom Come!
Hear the frogs a-chunkin' "Jug o' rum, Jug o' rum!"
Hear that mountain-whippoorwill be lonesome in the air,
An' I'll tell yuh how I traveled to the Essex County Fair.

Essex County has a mighty pretty fair,
All the smarty fiddlers from the South come there.

Elbows flyin' as they rosin up the bow
For the First Prize Contest in the Georgia Fiddlers' Show.

Old Dan Wheeling, with his whiskers in his ears,
King-pin fiddler for nearly twenty years.

Big Tom Sargent, with his blue wall-eye,
An' Little Jimmy Weezer that can make a fiddle cry.

All sittin' roun', spittin' high an' struttin' proud,
(Listen, little whippoorwill, yuh better bug yore eyes!)
Tun-a-tun-a-tunin' while the jedges told the crowd
Them that got the mostest claps 'd win the bestest prize.

Everybody waitin' for the first tweedle-dee,
When in comes a-stumblin'—hill-billy me!

Bowed right pretty to the jedges an' the rest,
Took a silver dollar from a hole inside my vest,

Plunked it on the table an' said, "There's my callin' card!
An' anyone that licks me—well, he's got to fiddle hard!"

Old Dan Wheeling, he was laughin' fit to holler,
Little Jimmy Weezer said, "There's one dead dollar!"

Big Tom Sargent had a yaller-toothy grin,
But I tucked my little whippoorwill spang underneath my
        chin,
An' petted it an' tuned it till the jedges said, "Begin!"

Big Tom Sargent was the first in line;
He could fiddle all the bugs off a sweet-potato vine.

He could fiddle down a possum from a mile-high tree.
He could fiddle up a whale from the bottom of the sea.

Yuh could hear hands spankin' till they spanked each other
      raw,
When he finished variations on "Turkey in the Straw."

Little Jimmy Weezer was the next to play;
He could fiddle all night, he could fiddle all day.

He could fiddle chills, he could fiddle fever,
He could make a fiddle rustle like a lowland river.

He could make a fiddle croon like a lovin' woman.
An' they clapped like thunder when he'd finished strummin'.

Then came the ruck of the bob-tailed fiddlers,
The let's go-easies, the fair-to-middlers.

They got their claps an' they lost their bicker,
An' settled back for some more corn-licker.

An' the crowd was tired of their no-count squealing,
When out in the center steps Old Dan Wheeling.

He fiddled high and he fiddled low,
(Listen, little whippoorwill; yuh got to spread yore wings!)
He fiddled with a cherrywood bow.
(Old Dan Wheeling's got bee-honey in his strings.)

He fiddled the wind by the lonesome moon,
He fiddled a most almighty tune.

He started fiddling like a ghost,
He ended fiddling like a host.

He fiddled north an' he fiddled south,
He fiddled the heart right out of yore mouth.

He fiddled here an' he fiddled there.
He fiddled salvation everywhere.

When he was finished, the crowd cut loose,
(Whippoorwill, they's rain on yore breast.)
An' I sat there wonderin', "What's the use?"
(Whippoorwill, fly home to yore nest.)

But I stood up pert an' I took my bow,
An' my fiddle went to my shoulder, so.

An'—they wasn't no crowd to get me fazed—
But I was alone where I was raised.

Up in the mountains, so still it makes yuh skeered.
Where God lies sleepin' in his big white beard.

An' I heard the sound of the squirrel in the pine,
An' I heard the earth a-breathin' thu' the long night-time.

They've fiddled the rose an' they've fiddled the thorn,
But they haven't fiddled the mountain-corn.

They've fiddled sinful an' fiddled moral,
But they haven't fiddled the breshwood-laurel.

They've fiddled loud, an' they've fiddled still,
But they haven't fiddled the whippoorwill.

I started off with a *dump-diddle-dump*,
(*Oh, Hell's broke loose in Georgia!*)
Skunk-cabbage growin' by the bee-gum stump,
(*Whippoorwill, yo're singin' now!*)

Oh, Georgia booze is mighty fine booze,
The best yuh ever poured yuh,
But it eats the soles right offen yore shoes,
For Hell's broke loose in Georgia.

My mother was a whippoorwill pert,
My father, he was lazy,
But I'm Hell broke loose in a new store shirt
To fiddle all Georgia crazy.

Swing yore partners—up an' down the middle!
Sashay now—oh, listen to that fiddle!
Flapjacks flippin' on a red-hot griddle,
An' Hell broke loose,
Hell broke loose,

Fire on the mountains—snakes in the grass.
Satan's here a-bilin'—oh, Lordy, let him pass!
Go down Moses, set my people free,
Pop goes the weasel thu' the old Red Sea!
Jonah sittin' on a hickory-bough,
Up jumps a whale—an' where's yore prophet now?
Rabbit in the pea-patch, possum in the pot,
Try an' stop my fiddle, now my fiddle's gettin' hot!
Whippoorwill, singin' thu' the mountain hush,
Whippoorwill, shoutin' from the burnin' bush,
Whippoorwill, cryin' in the stable-door,
Sing tonight as yuh never sang before!
Hell's broke loose like a stompin' mountain-shoat,
Sing till yuh bust the gold in yore throat!
Hell's broke loose for forty miles aroun'
Bound to stop yore music if yuh don't sing it **down.**
Sing on the mountains, little whippoorwill,
Sing to the valleys, an' slap 'em with a hill,
For I'm struttin' high as an eagle's quill,
An' Hell's broke loose,
Hell's broke loose,
Hell's broke loose in Georgia!

They wasn't a sound when I stopped bowin',
(*Whippoorwill, yuh can sing no more.*)
But, somewhere or other, the dawn was growin',
(*Oh, mountain whippoorwill!*)

An' I thought, "I've fiddled all night an' lost.
Yo're a good hill-billy, but yuh've been bossed."

So I went to congratulate old man Dan,
—But he put his fiddle into my han'—
An' then the noise of the crowd began.

Stephen Vincent Benét

JESSE JAMES

(A Design in Red and Yellow for a Nickel Library)

Jesse James was a two-gun man,
    (Roll on, Missouri!)
Strong-arm chief of an outlaw clan.
    (From Kansas to Illinois!)
He twirled an old Colt forty-five;
    (Roll on, Missouri!)
They never took Jesse James alive.
    (Roll, Missouri, roll!)

Jesse James was King of the Wes';
    (Cataracts in the Missouri!)
He'd a di'mon' heart in his lef' breas';
    (Brown Missouri rolls!)
He'd a fire in his heart no hurt could stifle:
    (Thunder, Missouri!)
Lion eyes an' a Winchester rifle.
    (Missouri, roll down!)

Jesse James rode a pinto hawse;
Come at night to a water-cawse;
Tetched with the rowel that pinto's flank;
She sprung the torrent from bank to bank.

Jesse rode through a sleepin' town;
Looked the moonlit street both up an' down;
Crack-crack-crack, the street ran flames
An' a great voice cried, "I'm Jesse James!"

Hawse an' afoot they're after Jess!
    (Roll on, Missouri!)

Spurrin' an' spurrin'—but he's gone Wes'.
      (*Brown Missouri rolls!*)
He was ten foot tall when he stood in his boots;
      (*Lightnin' like the Missouri!*)
More'n a match fer sich galoots.
      (*Roll, Missouri, roll!*)

Jesse James rode outa the sage;
Roun' the rocks come the swayin' stage;
Straddlin' the road a giant stan's
An' a great voice bellers, "Throw up yer han's!"

Jesse raked in the di'mon' rings,
The big gold watches an' the yuther things;
Jesse divvied 'em then an' thar
With a cryin' child had lost her mar.

They're creepin'; they're crawlin', they're stalkin' Jess;
      (*Roll on, Missouri!*)
They's a rumor he's gone much further Wes';
      (*Roll, Missouri, roll!*)
They's word of a cayuse hitched to the bars
      (*Ruddy clouds on Missouri!*)
Of a golden sunset that busts into stars.
      (*Missouri, roll down!*)

Jesse James rode hell fer leather;
He was a hawse an' a man together;
In a cave in a mountain high up in air
He lived with a rattlesnake, a wolf, an' a bear.

Jesse's heart was as sof' as a woman;
Fer guts an' stren'th he was sooper-human;
He could put six shots through a woodpecker's eye
And take in one swaller a gallon o' rye.

They sought him here an' they sought him there,
     (Roll on, Missouri!)
But he strides by night through the ways of the air;
     (Brown Missouri rolls!)
They say he was took an' they say he is dead,
     (Thunder, Missouri!)
But he ain't—he's a sunset overhead!
     (Missouri down to the sea!)

Jesse James was a Hercules.
When he went through the woods he tore up the trees.
When he went on the plains he smoked the groun'
An' the hull lan' shuddered fer miles aroun'.

Jesse James wore a red bandanner
That waved on the breeze like the Star Spangled Banner;
In seven states he cut up dadoes.
He's gone with the buffler an' the desperadoes.

Yes, Jesse James was a two-gun man
     (Roll on, Missouri!)
The same as when this song began;
     (From Kansas to Illinois!)
An' when you see a sunset bust into flames
     (Lightnin' like the Missouri!)
Or a thunderstorm blaze—that's Jesse James!
     (Hear that Missouri roll!)

                           William Rose Benét

THE GREEN GNOME

Ring, sing! ring, sing! pleasant Sabbath bells!
Chime, rhyme! chime, rhyme! through dales and dells!
Rhyme, ring! chime, sing! pleasant Sabbath bells!
Chime, sing! rhyme, ring! over fields and fells!

And I galloped and I galloped on my palfrey white as milk,
My robe was of the sea-green woof, my serk was of the silk;
My hair was golden-yellow, and it floated to my shoe;
My eyes were like two harebells bathed in little drops of
      dew;
My palfrey, never stopping, made a music sweetly blent
With the leaves of autumn dropping all around me as I
      went;
And I heard the bells, grown fainter, far behind me peal
      and play,
Fainter, fainter, fainter, till they seemed to die away;
And beside a silver runnel, on a little heap of sand,
I saw the green gnome sitting, with his cheek upon his
      hand.
Then he started up to see me, and he ran with a cry and
      bound,
And drew me from my palfrey white and set me on the
      ground.
O crimson, crimson were his locks, his face was green to
      see,
But he cried, "O light-haired lassie, you are bound to marry
      me!"
He clasped me round the middle small, he kissed me on
      the cheek,
He kissed me once, he kissed me twice, I could not stir or
      speak;

He kissed me twice, he kissed me thrice; but when he
    kissed again,
I called aloud upon the name of Him who died for men.

Sing, sing! ring, ring! pleasant Sabbath bells!
Chime, rhyme! chime, rhyme! through dales and dells!
Rhyme, ring! chime, sing! pleasant Sabbath bells!
Chime, sing! rhyme, ring! over fields and fells!

O faintly, faintly, faintly, calling men and maids to pray,
So faintly, faintly, faintly rang the bells far away;
And as I named the Blessed Name, as in our need we can,
The ugly green gnome became a tall and comely man:
His hands were white, his beard was gold, his eyes were
    black as sloes,
His tunic was of scarlet woof, and silken were his hose;
A pensive light from faëryland still lingered on his cheek,
His voice was like the running brook when he began to
    speak:
"O, you have cast away the charm my step-dame put on
    me,
Seven years have I dwelt in Faëryland, and you have set
    me free.
O, I will mount thy palfrey white, and ride to kirk with
    thee,
And, by those dewy little eyes, we twain will wedded be!"

Back we galloped, never stopping, he before and I behind,
And the autumn leaves were dropping, red and yellow in
    the wind;
And the sun was shining clearer, and my heart was high
    and proud,
As nearer, nearer, nearer rang the kirkbells sweet and loud,
And we saw the kirk, before us, as we trotted down the
    fells,
And nearer, nearer, o'er us, rang the welcome of the bells.

Ring, sing! ring, sing! pleasant Sabbath bells!
Chime, rhyme! chime, rhyme! through dales and dells!
Rhyme, ring! chime, sing! pleasant Sabbath bells!
Chime, sing! rhyme, ring! over fields and fells!

Robert Buchanan

GRANDFATHER WATTS'S
PRIVATE FOURTH

Grandfather Watts used to tell us boys
That a Fourth wa'n't a Fourth without any noise.
He would say, with a thump of his hickory stick,
That it made an American right down *sick*
To see his sons on the Nation's Day
Sit round, in a sort of a listless way,
With no oration and no train-band,
No fire-work show and no root-beer stand;
While his grandsons, before they were out of bibs,
Were ashamed—Great Scott!—to fire off squibs.

And so, each Independence morn,
Grandfather Watts took his powder-horn,
And the flint-lock shot-gun *his* father had
When he fought under Schuyler, a country lad;
And Grandfather Watts would start and tramp
Ten miles to the woods at Beaver Camp;
For Grandfather Watts used to say—and scowl—
That a decent chipmunk, or woodchuck, or owl
Was better company, friendly or shy,
Than folks who didn't keep Fourth of July.
And so he would pull his hat down on his brow,
And march for the woods, sou'-east by sou'.

But once—ah, long, long years ago,—
For Grandfather's gone where good men go,—
One hot, hot Fourth, by ways of our own
(Such short-cuts as boys have always known),
We hurried, and followed the dear old man
Beyond where the wilderness began—
To the deep black woods at the foot of the Hump;
And there was a clearing—and a stump.

A stump in the heart of a great wide wood,
And there on that stump our Grandfather stood,
Talking and shouting out there in the sun,
And firing that funny old flint-lock gun
Once in a minute—his head all bare—
Having his Fourth of July out there:
The Fourth of July that he used to know,
Back in eighteen-and-twenty or so!

First, with his face to the heavens blue,
He read the "Declaration" through;
And then, with gestures to left and right,
He made an oration erudite,
Full of words six syllables long—
And then our Grandfather burst into song!
And, scaring the squirrels in the trees,
Gave "Hail, Columbia!" to the breeze.

And I tell you the old man never heard
When we joined in the chorus, word for word!
But he sang out strong to the bright blue sky;
And if voices joined in his Fourth of July,
He heard them as echoes from days gone by.

And when he had done, we all slipped back,
As still as we came, on our twisting track,

While words more clear than the flint-lock shots
Rang in our ears.
                    And Grandfather Watts?

He shouldered the gun his father bore,
And marched off home, nor'-west by nor'.
                                        H. C. Bunner

THE ARROGANT FROG AND
THE SUPERIOR BULL

Once, on a time and in a place
    Conducive to malaria,
There lived a member of the race
    Of *Rana Temporaria;*
        Or, more concisely still, a frog
        Inhabited a certain bog.

A bull of Brobdingnagian size,
    Too proud for condescension,
One morning chanced to cast his eyes
    Upon the frog I mention;
        And, being to the manner born,
        Surveyed him with a lofty scorn.

Perceiving this, the bactrian's frame
    With anger was inflated,
Till, growing larger, he became
    Egregiously elated;
        For inspiration's sudden spell
        Had pointed out a way to swell.

"Ha, ha!" he proudly cried, "a fig
   For this, your mammoth torso!
Just watch me while I grow as big
   As you—or even more so!"
      To which magniloquential gush
      His bullship simply answered "Tush!"

Alas! the frog's success was slight,
   Which really was a wonder,
In view of how with main and might
   He strove to grow rotunder!
      And, standing patiently the while,
      The bull displayed a quiet smile.

But ah, the frog tried once too oft
   And, doing so, he busted;
Whereat the bull discreetly coughed
   And moved away, disgusted,
      As well he might, considering
      The wretched taste that marked the thing.

   THE MORAL: Everybody knows
      How ill a wind it is that blows.
                              Guy Wetmore Carryl

THE EMBARRASSING EPISODE OF LITTLE MISS MUFFET

Little Miss Muffet discovered a tuffet,
   (Which never occurred to the rest of us)
And, as 'twas a June day, and just about noonday,
   She wanted to eat—like the best of us:
Her diet was whey, and I hasten to say
   It is wholesome and people grow fat on it.

The spot being lonely, the lady not only
  Discovered the tuffet, but sat on it.

A rivulet gabbled beside her and babbled,
  As rivulets always are thought to do,
And dragon flies sported around and cavorted,
  As poets say dragon flies ought to do;
When, glancing aside for a moment, she spied
  A horrible sight that brought fear to her,
A hideous spider was sitting beside her,
  And most unavoidably near to her!

Albeit unsightly, this creature politely
  Said: "Madam, I earnestly vow to you,
I'm penitent that I did not bring my hat. I
  Should otherwise certainly bow to you."
Though anxious to please, he was so ill at ease
  That he lost all his sense of propriety,
And grew so inept that he clumsily stept
  In her plate—which is barred in Society.

This curious error completed her terror;
  She shuddered, and growing much paler, not
Only left her tuffet, but dealt him a buffet
  Which doubled him up in a sailor knot.
It should be explained that at this he was pained;
  He cried: "I have vexed you, no doubt of it!
Your fist's like a truncheon." "You're still in my luncheon,"
  Was all that she answered. "Get out of it!"

And the *Moral* is this: Be it madam or miss
  To whom you have something to say,
You are only absurd when you get in the curd,
  But you're rude when you get in the whey!

Guy Wetmore Carryl

THE GLORY TRAIL

'Way high up the Mogollons,
   Among the mountain tops,
A lion cleaned a yearlin's bones
   And licked his thankful chops,
When on the picture who should ride,
   A-trippin' down a slope,
But High-Chin Bob, with sinful pride
   And mav'rick-hungry rope.

    "Oh, glory be to me," says he,
      "And fame's unfadin' flowers!
    All meddlin' hands are far away;
    I ride my good top-hawse today
    And I'm top-rope of the Lazy J—
      Hi! kitty cut, you're ours!"

That lion licked his paw so brown
   And dreamed soft dreams of veal—
And then the circlin' loop sung down
   And roped him 'round his meal.
He yowled quick fury to the world
   Till all the hills yelled back;
The top-hawse gave a snort and whirled
   And Bob caught up the slack.

    "Oh, glory be to me," laughs he.
      "We've hit the glory trail.
    No human man as I have read
    Darst loop a ragin' lion's head,
    Nor ever hawse could drag one dead
      Until we told the tale."

'Way high up the Mogollons
　　That top-hawse done his best,
Through whippin' brush and rattlin' stones,
　　From canyon-floor to crest.
But ever when Bob turned and hoped
　　A limp remains to find,
A red-eyed lion, belly roped
　　But healthy, loped behind.

　　　"Oh, glory be to me," grunts he.
　　　　"This glory trail is rough,
　　　Yet even till the Judgment Morn
　　　I'll keep this dally 'round the horn,
　　　For never any hero born
　　　　Could stoop to holler: 'Nuff!' "

Three suns had rode their circle home
　　Beyond the desert's rim,
And turned their star-herds loose to roam
　　The ranges high and dim;
Yet up and down and 'round and 'cross
　　Bob pounded, weak and wan,
For pride still glued him to his hawse
　　And glory drove him on.

　　　"Oh, glory be to me," sighs he.
　　　　"He kaint be drug to death,
　　　But now I know beyond a doubt
　　　Them heroes I have read about
　　　Was only fools that stuck it out
　　　　To end of mortal breath."

'Way high up the Mogollons
　　A prospect man did swear
That moon dreams melted down his bones
　　And hoisted up his hair:

A ribby cow-hawse thundered by,
  A lion trailed along,
A rider, ga'nt but chin on high,
  Yelled out a crazy song.

"Oh, glory be to me!" cries he,
  "And to my noble noose!
Oh, stranger, tell my pards below
I took a rampin' dream in tow,
And if I never lay him low,
  I'll never turn him loose!"

                    Badger Clark

A LADY COMES TO AN INN

Three strange men came to the inn,
One was a black man pocked and thin,
One was brown with a silver knife,
And one brought with him a beautiful wife.

That lovely woman had hair as pale
As French champagne or finest ale,
That lovely woman was long and slim
As a young white birch or a maple limb.

Her face was like cream, her mouth was a rose,
What language she spoke nobody knows,
But sometimes she'd scream like a cockatoo
And swear wonderful oaths that nobody knew.

Her great silk skirts like a silver bell
Down to her little bronze slippers fell,
And her low-cut gown showed a dove on its nest
In blue tattooing across her breast.

Nobody learned the lady's name
Nor the marvellous land from which they came,
But no one in all the countryside
Has forgotten those men and that beautiful bride.
                    Elizabeth J. Coatsworth

THE PRINCESS AND THE GYPSIES

As I looked out one May morning
   I saw the tree-tops green;
I said: "My crown I will lay down
   And live no more a queen."

Then I tripped down my golden steps
   Dressed in my silken gown,
And when I stood in the open wood
   I met some gypsies brown.

"O gentle, gentle gypsies
   That roam the wide world through,
Because I hate my crown and state,
   O let me come with you!

"My councillors are old and gray
   And sit in narrow chairs,
But you can hear the birds sing clear
   And your hearts are as light as theirs."

"If you would come along with us
   Then you must count the cost,
For though in Spring the sweet birds sing,
   In Winter comes the frost.

"Your ladies serve you all the day
   With courtesy and care,
Your fine-shod feet they tread so neat
   But a gypsy's feet go bare.

"You wash in water running warm
   Through basins all of gold;
The streams where we roam have silvery foam,
   But the streams, the streams are cold.

"And barley bread is bitter to taste,
   Whilst sugary cakes they please.
Which will you choose, O which will you choose.
   Which will you choose of these?

"For if you choose the mountain streams
   And barley bread to eat,
Your heart will be free as the birds in the tree
   But the stones will cut your feet.

"The mud will spoil your silken gown
   And stain your insteps high,
The dogs in the farm will wish you harm
   And bark as you go by.

"And though your heart grow deep and gay
   And your heart grow wise and rich,
The cold will make your bones to ache
   And you will die in a ditch."

"O gentle, gentle gypsies
   That roam the wide world through,
Although I praise your wandering ways
   I dare not come with you."

I hung about their fingers brown
  My ruby rings and chain,
And with my head as heavy as lead
  I turned me back again.

As I went up the palace steps
  I heard the gypsies laugh;
The birds of Spring so sweet did sing,
  My heart it broke in half.

                              Frances Cornford

SHEEP

When I was once in Baltimore,
  A man came up to me and cried,
"Come, I have eighteen hundred sheep,
  And we will sail on Tuesday's tide.

"If you will sail with me, young man,
  I'll pay you fifty shillings down;
These eighteen hundred sheep I take
  From Baltimore to Glasgow town."

He paid me fifty shillings down,
  I sailed with eighteen hundred sheep;
We soon had cleared the harbor's mouth,
  We soon were in the salt sea deep.

The first night we were out at sea
  Those sheep were quiet in their mind;
The second night they cried with fear—
  They smelt no pastures in the wind.

They sniffed, poor things, for their green fields,
  They cried so loud I could not sleep:
For fifty thousand shillings down
  I would not sail again with sheep.
W. H. Davies

OFF THE GROUND

Three jolly Farmers
Once bet a pound
Each dance the others would
Off the ground.

Out of their coats
They slipped right soon,
And neat and nicesome,
Put each his shoon.

One—Two—Three!—
And away they go,
Not too fast,
And not too slow:
Out from the elm-tree's
Noonday shadow,
Into the sun
And across the meadow.
Past the schoolroom,
With knees well bent,
Fingers a-flicking,
They dancing went.
Up sides and over,
And round and round,
They crossed click-clacking,
The Parish bound.

By Tupman's meadow
They did their mile,
Tee-to-tum
On a three-barred stile.
Then straight through Whipham,
Downhill to Week,
Footing it lightsome,
But not too quick,
Up fields to Watchet,
And on through Wye,
Till seven fine churches
They'd seen skip by—
Seven fine churches,
And five old mills,
Farms in the valley,
And sheep on the hills;
Old Man's Acre
And Dead Man's Pool
All left behind,
As they danced through Wool.

And Wool gone by,
Like tops that seem
To spin in sleep
They danced in dream:
Withy—Wellover—
Wassop—Wo—
Like an old clock
Their heels did go.
A league and a league
And a league they went,
And not one weary,
And not one spent.
And lo! and behold!
Past Willow-cum-Leigh

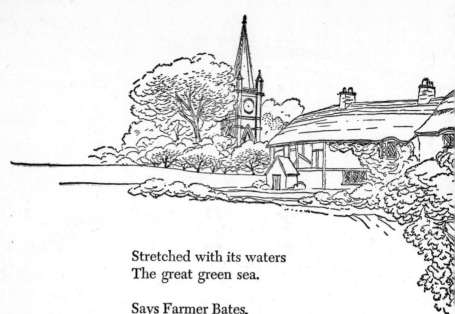

Stretched with its waters
The great green sea.

Says Farmer Bates,
"I puffs and I blows,
What's under the water,
Why, no man knows!"
Says Farmer Giles,
"My wind comes weak,
And a good man drownded
Is far to seek."
But Farmer Turvey,
On twirling toes
Ups with his gaiters,
And in he goes:
Down where the mermaids
Pluck and play
On their twangling harps
In a sea-green day;
Down where the mermaids,
Finned and fair,
Sleek with their combs
Their yellow hair. . . .

Bates and Giles—
On the shingle sat,
Gazing at Turvey's
Floating hat.
But never a ripple
Nor bubble told
Where he was supping
Off plates of gold.
Never an echo
Rilled through the sea
Of the feasting and dancing
And minstrelsy.
They called—called—called:
Came no reply:
Nought but the ripples'
Sandy sigh.
Then glum and silent
They sat instead,

Vacantly brooding
On home and bed,
Till both together
Stood up and said:—
"Us knows not, dreams not,
Where you be,
Turvey, unless
In the deep blue sea;
But axcusing silver—
And it comes most willing—
Here's us two paying
Our forty shilling;
For it's sartin sure, Turvey,
Safe and sound,
You danced us square, Turvey;
Off the ground!"

Walter de la Mare

HENRY VIII

Bluff King Hal was full of beans;
He married half a dozen queens;
For three called Kate they cried the banns,
And one called Jane, and a couple of Annes.

The first he asked to share his reign
Was Kate of Aragon, straight from Spain—
But when his love for her was spent,
He got a divorce, and out she went.

Anne Boleyn was his second wife;
He swore to cherish her all his life—
But seeing a third he wished instead,
He chopped off poor Anne Boleyn's head.

He married the next afternoon
Jane Seymour, which was rather soon—
But after one year as his bride
She crept into her bed and died.

Anne of Cleves was Number Four;
Her portrait thrilled him to the core—
But when he met her face to face
Another royal divorce took place.

Catherine Howard, Number Five,
Billed and cooed to keep alive—
But one day Henry felt depressed;
The executioner did the rest.

Sixth and last came Catherine Parr,
Sixth and last and luckiest far—
For this time it was Henry who
Hopped the twig, and a good job too.
                    Eleanor and *Herbert Farjeon*

THE DEATH OF ROBIN HOOD

"Give me my bow," said Robin Hood,
    "An arrow give to me;
And when 'tis shot mark thou that spot,
    For there my grave shall be."

Then Little John did make no sign,
    And not a word he spake;
But he smiled, altho' with mickle woe
    His heart was like to break.

He raised his master in his arms,
    And set him on his knee;
And Robin's eyes beheld the skies,
    The shaws, the greenwood tree.

The brook was babbling as of old,
    The birds sang full and clear,
And the wild-flowers gay like a carpet lay
    In the path of the timid deer.

"O Little John," said Robin Hood,
    "Meseemeth now to be
Standing with you so stanch and true
    Under the greenwood tree.

"And all around I hear the sound
    Of Sherwood long ago,
And my merry men come back again,—
    You know, sweet friend, you know!

"Now mark this arrow; where it falls,
    When I am dead dig deep,
And bury me there in the greenwood where
    I would forever sleep."

He twanged his bow. Upon its course
    The clothyard arrow sped,
And when it fell in yonder dell,
    Brave Robin Hood was dead.

The sheriff sleeps in a marble vault,
    The king in a shroud of gold;
And upon the air with a chanted pray'r
    Mingles the mock of mould.

But the deer draw to the shady pool,
   The birds sing blithe and free,
And the wild-flow'rs bloom o'er a hidden tomb
   Under the greenwood tree.

Eugene Field

SONG OF THE ALL-WOOL SHIRT

My father bought an undershirt
   Of bright and flaming red—
"All wool, I'm ready to assert,
   Fleece-dyed," the merchant said;
"Your size is thirty-eight, I think;
   A forty you should get,
Since all-wool goods are bound to shrink
   A trifle when they're wet."

That shirt two weeks my father wore—
   Two washings, that was all;
From forty down to thirty-four
   It shrank like leaf in fall.
I wore it then a day or two,
   But when 'twas washed again
My wife said, "Now 'twill only do
   For little brother Ben."

A fortnight Ben squeezed into it;
   At last he said it hurt.
We put it on our babe—the fit
   Was good as any shirt.
We ne'er will wash it more while yet
   We see its flickering light,
For if again that shirt is wet
   'Twill vanish from our sight.

Eugene Field

THE GREEN FIDDLER

As I came over the humpbacked hill
　Where the trees crowd thick and black,
I met a little old man in green
　With fiddle strapped on back.

His cap rose tall as an Elfin steeple,
　His eyes shone water clear,
He bowed him low to see me go
　And he said to me, "My dear,

"It's not for silver I'm asking you,
　For shelter or meat or bread,
But pluck me four of your golden hairs,
　Four bright golden hairs," he said.

"It's a little thing to ask," thought I.
　"You're welcome enough to mine."
On the wood road dim, I gave them him.
　He smiled to see them shine.

He reached the fiddle from off his back,
　He threaded them one by one,
Brighter than golden wire they gleamed,
　Finer than silk new spun.

Then swift as shadow the thin bow flew.
　His fingers capered gay;
Birds, far and near, grew still to hear
　That elfin fiddler play.

And shy wood creatures with still bright gaze
　On soundless tread crept near,
The very leaves hung motionless
　Above my head to hear.

I could not feel my own heart beat,
  The breath died in my throat;
Stock still I stood in the shadowed wood,
  Lest I should miss one note.

Twilight came stealing from tree to tree,
  The little lights of town
Sprinkled the valley like buttercups,
  Or stars turned upside down;

And the fartherest one that I knew for mine,
  It would not let me stay;
Oh, the tune was sweet, but my town-weighed feet,
  They carried me away.

Carried me home to the valley lights,
  To the ticking clock on the stair,
To fire and cupboard and table spread
  With damask and willow ware.

So I laugh and gossip by candlelight
  To the clatter of plate and spoon,
But my cheeks turn hot for a secret spot
  And the lilt of a fairy tune.

And wherever I go and whatever I do
  Silvery, wild, and shrill,
I am hearing that little old man in green
  On the side of the humpbacked hill.

The neighbors may frown and shake their heads
  To see me stand and stare.
What should they know of fiddle bow
  And strings of golden hair?

Oh, I let them scold and I let them smile,
    And whisper of me apart,
For I have a hidden fairy tune
    In the bottom of my heart.

                              Rachel Field

THE OWL-CRITIC

"Who stuffed that white owl?" No one spoke in the shop:
The barber was busy, and he couldn't stop;
The customers, waiting their turns, were all reading
The *Daily*, the *Herald*, the *Post*, little heeding
The young man who blurted out such a blunt question;
Not one raised a head, or even made a suggestion;
            And the barber kept on shaving.

"Don't you see, Mister Brown,"
Cried the youth, with a frown,
"How wrong the whole thing is,
How preposterous each wing is,
How flattened the head is, how jammed down the neck is—
In short, the whole owl, what an ignorant wreck 'tis!
I make no apology;
I've learned owl-eology.
I've passed days and nights in a hundred collections,
And cannot be blinded to any deflections
Arising from unskilful fingers that fail
To stuff a bird right, from his beak to his tail.
Mister Brown! Mister Brown!
Do take that bird down,
Or you'll soon be the laughing-stock all over town!"
            And the barber kept on shaving.

"I've *studied* owls
And other night fowls,
And I tell you
What I know to be true:
An owl cannot roost
With his limbs so unloosed;
No owl in this world
Ever had his claws curled,
Ever had his legs slanted,
Ever had his bill canted,
Ever had his neck screwed
Into that attitude.
He can't *do* it, because
'Tis against all bird-laws.
Anatomy teaches,
Ornithology preaches
An owl has a toe
That *can't* turn out so!
I've made the white owl my study for years,
And to see such a job almost moves me to tears!
Mister Brown, I'm amazed
You should be so gone crazed
As to put up a bird
In that posture absurd!
To *look* at that owl really brings on a dizziness;
The man who stuffed *him* don't half know his business!"
     And the barber kept on shaving.

"Examine those eyes.
I'm filled with surprise
Taxidermists should pass
Off on you such poor glass;
So unnatural they seem
They'd make Audubon scream,

And John Burroughs laugh
To encounter such chaff.
Do take that bird down;
Have him stuffed again, Brown!"
      And the barber kept on shaving.

"With some sawdust and bark
I would stuff in the dark
An owl better than that;
I could make an old hat
Look more like an owl
Than that horrid fowl,
Stuck up there so stiff like a side of coarse leather.
In fact, about *him* there's not one natural feather."

Just then, with a wink and a sly normal lurch,
The owl, very gravely, got down from his perch,
Walked round, and regarded his fault-finding critic
(Who thought he was stuffed) with a glance analytic,
And then fairly hooted, as if he should say:
"Your learning's at fault *this* time, anyway;
Don't waste it again on a live bird, I pray.
I'm an owl; you're another. Sir Critic, good-day!"
      And the barber kept on shaving.
          James Thomas Fields

LORD ARNALDOS

¿Quién hubiese tal ventura?

The strangest of adventures,
That happen by the sea,
Befell to Lord Arnaldos
On the Evening of St. John;
For he was out a-hunting—
A huntsman bold was he!—
When he beheld a little ship
And close to land was she.
Her cords were all of silver,
Her sails of cramasy;
And he who sailed the little ship
Was singing at the helm:
The waves stood still to hear him,
The wind was soft and low;
The fish who dwell in darkness
Ascended through the sea,
And all the birds in heaven
Flew down to his mast-tree.
Then spake the Lord Arnaldos,
(Well shall you hear his words!)
"Tell me for God's sake, sailor,
What song may that song be?"
The sailor spake in answer,
And answer thus made he:
"I only tell my song to those
Who sail away with me."
                    James Elroy Flecker

BROWN'S DESCENT

or, the Willy-nilly Slide

Brown lived at such a lofty farm
    That everyone for miles could see
His lantern when he did his chores
    In winter after half-past three.

And many must have seen him make
    His wild descent from there one night,
'Cross lots, 'cross walls, 'cross everything,
    Describing rings of lantern light.

Between the house and barn the gale
    Got him by something he had on
And blew him out on the icy crust
    That cased the world, and he was gone!

Walls were all buried, trees were few:
    He saw no stay unless he stove
A hole in somewhere with his heel.
    But though repeatedly he strove

And stamped and said things to himself,
    And sometimes something seemed to yield,
He gained no foothold, but pursued
    His journey down from field to field.

Sometimes he came with arms outspread
    Like wings, revolving in the scene
Upon his longer axis, and
    With no small dignity of mien.

Faster or slower as he chanced,
    Sitting or standing as he chose,

According as he feared to risk
   His neck, or thought to spare his clothes.

He never let the lantern drop.
   And some exclaimed who saw afar
The figures he described with it,
   "I wonder what those signals are

Brown makes at such an hour of night!
   He's celebrating something strange.
I wonder if he's sold his farm,
   Or been made Master of the Grange."

He reeled, he lurched, he bobbed, he checked;
   He fell and made the lantern rattle
(But saved the light from going out.)
   So half-way down he fought the battle,

Incredulous of his own bad luck.
   And then becoming reconciled
To everything, he gave it up
   And came down like a coasting child.

"Well—I—be—" that was all he said,
   As standing in the river road,
He looked back up the slippery slope
   (Two miles it was) to his abode.

Sometimes as an authority
   On motor-cars, I'm asked if I
Should say our stock was petered out,
   And this is my sincere reply:

Yankees are what they always were.
   Don't think Brown ever gave up hope

Of getting home again because
    He couldn't climb that slippery slope;

Or even thought of standing there
    Until the January thaw
Should take the polish off the crust.
    He bowed with grace to natural law,

And then went round it on his feet,
    After the manner of our stock;
Not much concerned for those to whom,
    At that particular time o'clock,

It must have looked as if the course
    He steered was really straight away
From that which he was headed for—
    Not much concerned for them, I say;

No more so than became a man—
    And politician at odd seasons.
I've kept Brown standing in the cold
    While I invested him with reasons;

But now he snapped his eyes three times;
    Then shook his lantern, saying, "Ile's
'Bout out!" and took the long way home
    By road, a matter of several miles.
                              Robert Frost

THE HIGHWAYMAN'S GHOST

Twelve o'clock—a misty night—
Glimpsing hints of buried light—
Six years strung in an iron chain—
Time I stood on the ground again!

So—by your leave! Slip, easy enough,
Withered wrists from the rusty cuff.
The old chain rattles, the old wood groans,
O the clatter of clacking bones!

Here I am, uncoated, unhatted,
Shirt all mildewed, hair all matted,
Sockets that each have royally
Fed the crow with a precious eye.

O for slashing Bess the brown!
Where, old lass, have they earthed thee down?
Sobb'st beneath a carrier's thong?
Strain'st a coalman's cart along?

Shame to foot it!—must be so.
See, the mists are smitten below;
Over the moorland, wide away,
Moonshine pours her watery day.

There the long white-dusted track,
There a crawling speck of black.
The Northern mail, ha, ha! and he
There on the box is Anthony.

Coachman I scared him from brown to grey,
Witness he lied my blood away.
Haste, Fred! haste, boy! never fail!
Now or never! catch the mail!

The horses plunge, and sweating stop.
Dead falls Tony, neck and crop.
Nay, good guard, small profit thus,
Shooting ghosts with a blunderbuss!

Crash wheel! coach over! How it rains
Hampers, ladies, wigs, and canes!
O the spoil! to sack it and lock it!
But, woe is me, I have never a pocket!

Richard Garnett

THE FIGURE-HEAD

A Salt Sea Yarn

There was an ancient carver that carved of a saint,
But the parson wouldn't have it, so he took a pot of paint
And changed its angel garment for a dashing soldier rig,
And said it was a figure-head and sold it to a brig.

The brig hauled her mainsail to an off-shore draught,
Then she shook her snowy royals and the Scillies went
     abaft;
And cloudy with her canvas she ran before the Trade
Till she got to the Equator, where she struck a merrymaid.

A string of pearls and conches were all of her togs,
But the flying-fish and porpoises they followed her like
     dogs;
She had a voice of silver and lips of coral red,
She climbed the dolphin-striker and kissed the figure-head.

Then every starry evening she'd swim in the foam
About the bows, a-singing like a nightingale at Home;
She'd call to him and sing to him as sweetly as a bird;
But the wooden-headed effigy he never said a word.

And every starry evening in the Doldrum calms
She'd wriggle up the bobstay and throw her tender arms
About his scarlet shoulders and fondle him and cry
And stroke his curly whiskers, but he never winked an eye.

She couldn't get an answer to her tears or moans,
So she went and told her Daddy, told the ancient Davy
    Jones;
Old Davy damned his eyesight and puzzled of his wits,
Then whistled up his hurricanes and tore the brig to bits.

Down on the ocean-bed, green fathoms deep,
Where the wrecks lie rotting and great sea-serpents creep,
In a gleaming grotto all built of sailors' bones,
Sits the handsome figure-head, listening to Miss Jones.

Songs o' love she sings him the livelong day,
And she hangs upon his bosom and sobs the night away,
But he never, never answers, for beneath his soldier paint
The wooden-headed lunatic still thinks that he's a saint.

Crosbie Garstin

FLANNAN ISLE

"Though three men dwell on Flannan Isle
To keep the lamp alight,
As we steered under the lee, we caught
No glimmer through the night."—

A passing ship at dawn had brought
The news; and quickly we set sail,
To find out what strange thing might ail
The keepers of the deep-sea light.

The Winter day broke blue and bright,
With glancing sun and glancing spray,
While o'er the swell our boat made way,
As gallant as a gull in flight.

But as we neared the lonely Isle,
And looked up at the naked height,
And saw the lighthouse towering white,
With blinded lantern, that all night
Had never shot a spark
Of comfort through the dark,
So ghostly in the cold sunlight
It seemed, that we were struck the while
With wonder all too dread for words.

And as into the tiny creek
We stole beneath the hanging crag,
We saw three queer, black, ugly birds—
Too big, by far, in my belief,
For cormorant or shag—
Like seamen sitting bolt-upright
Upon a half-tide reef:
But, as we neared, they plunged from sight,
Without a sound, or spurt of white.

And still too mazed to speak,
We landed; and made fast the boat;
And climbed the track in single file,
Each wishing he were safe afloat,
On any sea, however far,
So it be far from Flannan Isle:
And still we seemed to climb, and climb,
As though we'd lost all count of time,
And so must climb for evermore.
Yet, all too soon, we reached the door

The black, sun-blistered lighthouse-door,
That gaped for us ajar.

As, on the threshold, for a spell,
We paused, we seemed to breathe the smell
Of limewash and of tar,
Familiar as our daily breath,
As though 'twere some strange scent of death:
And so, yet wondering, side by side,
We stood a moment, still tongue-tied:
And each with black foreboding eyed
The door, ere we should fling it wide,
To leave the sunlight for the gloom:
Till, plucking courage up, at last,
Hard on each other's heels we passed,
Into the living-room.

Yet, as we crowded through the door,
We only saw a table, spread
For dinner, meat and cheese and bread;
But, all untouched; and no one there:
As though, when they sat down to eat,
Ere they could even taste,
Alarm had come; and they in haste
Had risen and left the bread and meat:
For at the table-head a chair
Lay tumbled on the floor.
We listened; but we only heard
The feeble cheeping of a bird
That starved upon its perch:
And, listening still, without a word,
We set about our hopeless search.

We hunted high, we hunted low;
And soon ransacked the empty house;

Then o'er the Island, to and fro,
We ranged, to listen and to look
In every cranny, cleft or nook
That might have hid a bird or mouse:
But, though we searched from shore to shore,
We found no sign in any place:
And soon again stood face to face
Before the gaping door:
And stole into the room once more
As frightened children steal.
Ay: though we hunted high and low,
And hunted everywhere,
Of the three men's fate we found no trace
Of any kind in any place,
But a door ajar, and an untouched meal,
And an overtoppled chair.
And as we listened in the gloom
Of that forsaken living-room—
A chill clutch on our breath—
We thought how ill-chance came to all
Who kept the Flannan Light:
And how the rock had been the death
Of many a likely lad:
How six had come to a sudden end,
And three had gone stark mad:
And one whom we'd all known as friend
Had leapt from the lantern one still night,
And fallen dead by the lighthouse wall:
And long we thought
On the three we sought,
And of what might yet befall.
Like curs a glance has brought to heel,
We listened, flinching there:
And looked, and looked, on the untouched meal,
And the overtoppled chair.

We seemed to stand for an endless while,
Though still no word was said,
Three men alive on Flannan Isle,
Who thought on three men dead.

                                    W. W. Gibson

THERE LIVED A KING

There lived a King, as I've been told,
In the wonder-working days of old,
When hearts were twice as good as gold,
    And twenty times as mellow.
Good-temper triumphed in his face,
And in his heart he found a place
For all the erring human race
    And every wretched fellow.
When he had Rhenish wine to drink
It made him very sad to think
That some, at junket or at jink,
    Must be content with toddy.
He wished all men as rich as he
(And he was rich as rich could be),
So to the top of every tree
    Promoted everybody.

Lord Chancellors were cheap as sprats,
And Bishops in their shovel hats
Were plentiful as tabby cats—
    In point of fact, too many.
Ambassadors cropped up like hay,
Prime Ministers and such as they
Grew like asparagus in May,
    And Dukes were three a penny.

On every side Field Marshals gleamed,
Small beer were Lords Lieutenant deemed,
With Admirals the ocean teemed
   All round his wide dominions.
And Party Leaders you might meet
In twos and threes in every street,
Maintaining, with no little heat,
   Their various opinions.

That King, although no one denies
His heart was of abnormal size,
Yet he'd have acted otherwise
   If he had been acuter.
The end is easily foretold,
When every blessed thing you hold
Is made of silver, or of gold,
   You long for simple pewter.
When you have nothing else to wear
But cloth of gold and satins rare,
For cloth of gold you cease to care—
   Up goes the price of shoddy.
In short, whoever you may be,
To this conclusion you'll agree,
When every one is somebodee,
   Then no one's anybody!
              W. S. Gilbert

THE PERILS OF INVISIBILITY

Old PETER led a wretched life—
Old PETER had a furious wife;
Old PETER, too, was truly stout,
He measured several yards about.

The little fairy PICKLEKIN
One summer afternoon looked in,
And said, "Old PETER, how-de-do?
Can I do anything for you?

"I have three gifts—the first will give
Unbounded riches while you live;
The second, health where'er you be;
The third, invisibility."

"O, little fairy PICKLEKIN,"
Old PETER answered, with a grin,
"To hesitate would be absurd,—
Undoubtedly I choose the third."

" 'Tis yours," the fairy said, "be quite
Invisible to mortal sight
Whene'er you please. Remember me
Most kindly, pray to MRS. P."

Old MRS. PETER overheard
Wee PICKLEKIN's concluding word,
And, jealous of her girlhood's choice,
Said, "That was some young woman's voice!"

Old PETER let her scold and swear—
Old PETER, bless him, didn't care.
"My dear, your rage is wasted quite—
Observe, I disappear from sight!"

A well-bred fairy (so I've heard)
Is always faithful to her word:
Old PETER vanished like a shot,
But then—*his suit of clothes did not.*

For when conferred the fairy slim
Invisibility on him,
She popped away on fairy wings,
Without referring to his "things."

So there remained a coat of blue,
A vest and double eyeglass too,
His tail, his shoes, his socks as well,
His pair of—no, I must not tell.

Old Mrs. PETER soon began
To see the failure of his plan,
And then resolved (I quote the bard)
To "hoist him with his own petard."

Old PETER woke next day and dressed,
Put on his coat and shoes and vest,
His shirt and stock—*but could not find*
His only pair of—never mind!

Old PETER was a decent man,
And though he twigged his lady's plan,
Yet, hearing her approaching, he
Resumed invisibility.

"Dear Mrs. P., my only joy,"
Exclaimed the horrified old boy;
"Now give them up, I beg of you—
You know what I'm referring to!"

But no; the cross old lady swore
She'd keep his—what I said before—
To make him publicly absurd;
And Mrs. PETER kept her word.

The poor old fellow had no rest;
His coat, his stock, his shoes, his vest,
Were all that now met mortal eye—
The rest, invisibility!

"Now, madam, give them up, I beg—
I've bad rheumatics in my leg;
Besides, until you do, it's plain
I cannot come to sight again!

"For though some mirth it might afford
To see my clothes without their lord,
Yet there would rise indignant oaths
If he were seen without his clothes!"

But no; resolved to have her quiz,
The lady held her own—and his—
And PETER left his humble cot
To find a pair of—you know what.

But—here's the worst of this affair—
Whene'er he came across a pair
Already placed for him to don,
He was too stout to get them on!

So he resolved at once to train,
And walked and walked with all his main;
For years he paced this mortal earth,
To bring himself to decent girth.

At night, when all around is still,
You'll find him pounding up a hill;
And shrieking peasants whom he meets,
Fall down in terror on the peats!

Old PETER walks through wind and rain
Resolved to train, and train, and train,
Until he weighs twelve stone or so—
And when he does, I'll let you know.

W. S. Gilbert

FINNIGIN TO FLANNIGAN

Superintindint was Flannigan;
Boss av the siction was Finnigin;
Whiniver the kyars got offen the thrack
An' muddled up things t' th' divil an' back,
Finnigin writ it to Flannigan,
Afther the wrick wuz all on agin;
That is, this Finnigin
Repoorted to Flannigan.

Whin Finnigin furst writ to Flannigan,
He writed tin pages—did Finnigin.
An' he tould jist how the smash occurred;
Full minny a tajus, blunderin' wurrd
Did Finnigin write to Flannigan
Afther the cars had gone on agin.
That wuz how Finnigin
Repoorted to Flannigan.

Now Flannigan knowed more than Finnigin—
He'd more idjucation—had Flannigan;
An' it wore'm clane an' complately out
To tell what Finnigin writ about
In his writin' to Muster Flannigan.
So he writed back to Finnigin:
"Don't do sich a sin agin;
Make 'em brief, Finnigin!"

Whin Finnigin got this from Flannigan,
He blushed rosy rid—did Finnigin;
An' he said: "I'll gamble a whole month's **pa-ay**
That it will be minny an' minny a da-ay
Befoore Sup'rintindint, that's Flannigan,
Gits a whack at this very same sin agin.
From Finnigin to Flannigan
Repoorts won't be long agin."

Wan da-ay on the siction av Finnigin,
On the road sup'rintinded by Flannigan,
A rail gave way on a bit av a curve
An' some kyars went off as they made the swerve,
"There's nobody hurted," sez Finnigin,
"But repoorts must be made to Flannigan."
An' he winked at McGorrigan,
As married a Finnigin.

He wuz shantyin' thin wuz Finnigin,
As minny a railroader's been agin,
An' the shmoky ol' lamp wuz burnin' bright
In Finnigin's shanty all that night—
Bilin' down his repoort, was Finnigin!
An' he writed this here: "Muster Flannigan:
Off agin, on agin,
Gone agin.—Finnigin."

S. W. Gillilan

THE DOG'S COLD NOSE

When Noah, perceiving 'twas time to embark,
Persuaded the creatures to enter the Ark,
The dog, with a friendliness truly sublime,
Assisted in herding them. Two at a time

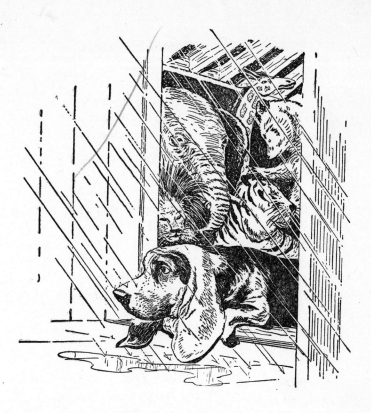

He drove in the elephants, zebras and gnus
Until they were packed like a boxful of screws,
The cat in the cupboard, the mouse on the shelf,
The bug in the crack; then he backed in himself.
But such was the lack of available space
He couldn't tuck all of him into the place;
So after the waters had flooded the plain
And down from the heavens fell blankets of rain
He stood with his muzzle thrust out through the door
The whole forty days of that terrible pour!
Because of which drenching, zoologists hold,
The nose of a healthy dog always is cold!

Arthur Guiterman

THE SPELLING BEE AT ANGELS

(Reported by Truthful James)

Waltz in, waltz in, ye little kids, and gather round my
    knee,
And drop them books and first pot-hooks, and hear a yarn
    from me.
I kin not sling a fairy tale of Jinnys fierce and wild,
For I hold it is unchristian to deceive a simple child;
But as from school yer driftin' by, I thowt ye'd like to hear
Of a "Spelling Bee" at Angels that we organized last year.

It warn't made up of gentle kids, of pretty kids, like you,
But gents ez hed their reg'lar growth, and some enough
    for two.
There woz Lanky Jim of Sutter's Fork and Bilson of La-
    grange,
And "Pistol Bob," who wore that day a knife by way of
    change.
You start, you little kids, you think these are not pretty
    names,
But each had a man behind it, and—my name is Truthful
    James.

There was Poker Dick from Whisky Flat, and Smith of
    Shooter's Bend,
And Brown of Calaveras—which I want no better friend;
Three-fingered Jack—yes, pretty dears, three fingers—
    you have five.
Clapp cut off two—it's sing'lar, too, that Clapp ain't now
    alive.
'Twas very wrong indeed, my dears, and Clapp was much
    to blame;
Likewise was Jack, in after-years, for shootin' of that same.

The nights was kinder lengthenin' out, the rains had jest
    begun,
When all the camp came up to Pete's to have their usual
    fun;
But we all sot kinder sad-like around the bar-room stove
Till Smith got up, permiskiss-like, and this remark he
    hove:
"Thar's a new game down in Frisco, that ez far ez I can
    see
Beats euchre, poker, and van-toon, they calls the 'Spellin'
    Bee.'"

Then Brown of Calaveras simply hitched his chair and
    spake,
"Poker is good enough for me," and Lanky Jim sez,
    "Shake!"
And Bob allowed he warn't proud, but he "must say right
    thar
That the man who tackled euchre hed his education
    squar."
This brought up Lenny Fairchild, the schoolmaster, who
    said
He knew the game, and he would give instructions on that
    head.

"For instance, take some simple word," sez he, "like
    'separate':
Now who can spell it?" Dog my skin, ef thar was one in
    eight.
This set the boys all wild at once. The chairs was put in
    row,
And at the head was Lanky Jim, and at the foot was Joe,
And high upon the bar itself the schoolmaster was raised,
And the bar-keep put his glasses down, and sat and silent
    gazed.

The first word out was "parallel," and seven let it be,
Till Joe waltzed in his "double l" betwixt the "a" and
    "e";
For since he drilled them Mexicans in San Jacinto's fight
Thar warn't no prouder man got up than Pistol Joe that
    night—
Till "rhythm" came! He tried to smile, then said "they
    had him there,"
And Lanky Jim, with one long stride, got up and took his
    chair.

O little kids, my pretty kids, 'twas touchin' to survey
These bearded men, with weppings on, like schoolboys at
    their play.
They'd laugh with glee, and shout to see each other lead
    the van,
And Bob sat up as monitor with a cue for a rattan,
Till the Chair gave out "incinerate," and Brown said he'd
    be durned
If any such blamed word as that in school was ever
    learned.

When "phthisis" came they all sprang up, and vowed the
    man who rung
Another blamed Greek word on them be taken out and
    hung.
As they sat down again I saw in Bilson's eye a flash,
And Brown of Calaveras was a-twistin' his mustache,
And when at last Brown slipped on "gneiss," and Bilson
    took his chair,
He dropped some casual words about some folks who
    dyed their hair.

And then the Chair grew very white, and the Chair said
    he'd adjourn,
But Poker Dick remarked that *he* would wait and get his
    turn;

Then with a tremblin' voice and hand, and with a wan-
derin' eye,
The Chair next offered "eider-duck," and Dick began with
"I,"
And Bilson smiled—then Bilson shrieked! Just how the
fight begun
I never knowed, for Bilson dropped, and Dick, he moved
up one.

Then certain gents arose and said "they'd business down
in camp,"
And "ez the road was rather dark, and ez the night was
damp,
They'd"—here got up Three-fingered Jack and locked the
door and yelled:
"No, not one mother's son goes out till that thar word is
spelled!"
But while the words were on his lips, he groaned and sank
in pain,
And sank with Webster on his chest and Worcester on his
brain.

Below the bar dodged Poker Dick, and tried to look ez he
Was huntin' up authorities thet no one else could see;
And Brown got down behind the stove, allowin' he "was
cold,"
Till it upsot and down his legs the cinders freely rolled,
And several gents called "Order!" till in his simple way
Poor Smith began with "O-r"—"Or"—and he was dragged
away.

O little kids, my pretty kids, down on your knees and
pray!
You've got your eddication in a peaceful sort of way;
And bear in mind thar may be sharps ez slings their spellin'
square,

But likewise slings their bowie-knives without a thought
    or care.
You wants to know the rest, my dears? Thet's all! In
    me you see
The only gent that lived to tell about the Spellin' Bee!

He ceased and passed, that truthful man; the children
    went their way
With downcast heads and downcast hearts—but not to
    sport or play.
For when at eve the lamps were lit, and supperless to bed
Each child was sent, with tasks undone and lessons all
    unsaid,
No man might know the awful woe that thrilled their
    youthful frames,
As they dreamed of Angels' Spelling Bee and thought of
    Truthful James.

                                                    Bret Harte

THE FALL OF J. W. BEANE

A Ghost Story

In all the Eastern hemisphere
You wouldn't find a knight, a peer,
A viscount, earl or baronet,
A marquis or a duke, nor yet
A prince, or emperor, or king,
Or sultan, czar, or anything
That could in family pride surpass
J. Wentworth Beane of Boston, Mass.
His family tree could far outscale
The bean-stalk in the fairy tale;

And Joseph's coat would pale before
The blazon'd coat-of-arms he bore,
The arms of his old ancestor,
One Godfrey Beane, "who crossed, you know,
About two hundred years ago."
He had it stamped, engraved, embossed,
Without the least regard to cost,
Upon his house, upon his gate,
Upon his table-cloth, his plate,
Upon his knocker, and his mat,
Upon his watch, inside his hat;
On scarf-pin, handkerchief, and screen,
And cards; in short, J. Wentworth Beane
Contrived to have old Godfrey's crest
On everything that he possessed.
And lastly, when he died, his will
Proved to contain a codicil
Directing that a sum be spent
To carve it on his monument.

But if you think this ends the scene
You little know J. Wentworth Beane.
To judge him by the common host
Is reckoning without his ghost.
And it is something that befell
His ghost I chiefly have to tell.

At midnight of the very day
They laid J. Wentworth Beane away,
No sooner had the clock come round
To 12 P. M. than from the ground
Arose a spectre, lank and lean,
With frigid air and haughty mien;

No other than J. Wentworth Beane,
Unchanged in all, except his pride—
If anything, intensified.

He looked about him with that air
Of supercilious despair
That very stuck-up people wear
At some society affair
When no one in their set is there.
Then, after brushing from his sleeves
Some bits of mould and clinging leaves,
And lightly dusting off his shoe,
The iron gate he floated through,
Just looking back the clock to note,
As one who fears to miss a boat.
Ten minutes later found him on
The ghost's Cunarder—"Oregon";
And ten days later by spook time
He heard the hour of midnight chime
From out the tower of Beanley Hall,
And stood within the grave-yard wall
Beside a stone, moss-grown and green,
On which these simple words were seen:

IN MEMORY
SIR GODFREY BEANE

The while he gazed in thought serene
A little ghost of humble mien,
Unkempt and crooked, bent and spare,
Accosted him with cringing air:
"Most noble sir, 'tis plain to see
You are not of the likes of me;
You are a spook of high degree."

"My good man," cried J. Wentworth B.,
"Leave me a little while, I pray,
I've travelled very far to-day,
And I desire to be alone
With him who sleeps beneath this stone.
I cannot rest till I have seen
My ancestor, Sir Godfrey Beane."

"Your ancestor! How can that be?"
Exclaimed the little ghost, "when he,
Last of his line, was drowned at sea
Two hundred years ago; this stone
Is to his memory alone.
I, and I only, saw his end.
As he, my master and my friend,
Leaned o'er the vessel's side one night
I pushed him—no, it was not right,
I own that I was much to blame;
I donned his clothes, and took the name
Of Beane—I also took his gold,
About five thousand pounds all told;
And so to Boston, Mass., I came
To found a family and name—
I, who in former times had been
Sir Godfrey's—"

                    "Wretch, what do you mean!
Sir Godfrey's what?" gasped Wentworth Beane.
"Sir Godfrey's valet!"

                    That same night,
When the ghost steamer sailed, you might
Among the passengers have seen
A ghost of very abject mien,

Faded and shrunk, forlorn and frayed,
The shadow of his former shade,
Who registered in steerage class,
J. W. Beane of Boston, Mass.

Now, gentle reader, do not try
To guess the family which I
Disguise as Beane—enough that they
Exist on Beacon Hill to-day,
In sweet enjoyment of their claims—
It is not well to mention names.

Oliver Herford

THE DEACON'S MASTERPIECE

or, the Wonderful "One-hoss Shay"

Have you heard of the wonderful one-hoss shay,
That was built in such a logical way
It ran a hundred years to a day,
And then, of a sudden, it—ah, but stay,
I'll tell you what happened without delay,
Scaring the parson into fits,
Frightening people out of their wits,—
Have you ever heard of that, I say?

Seventeen hundred and fifty-five,
Georgius Secundus was then alive,—
Snuffy old drone from the German hive;
That was the year when Lisbon-town
Saw the earth open and gulp her down,
And Braddock's army was done so brown,
Left without a scalp to its crown.
It was on the terrible Earthquake-day
That the Deacon finished the one-hoss shay.

Now in building of chaises, I tell you what,
There is always *somewhere* a weakest spot,—
In hub, tire, felloe, in spring or thill,
In panel, or crossbar, or floor, or sill,
In screw, bolt, thoroughbrace,—lurking still,
Find it somewhere you must and will,—
Above or below, within or without,—
And that's the reason, beyond a doubt,
That a chaise *breaks down*, but doesn't *wear out.*

But the Deacon swore, (as Deacons do,
With an "I dew vum," on an "I tell *yeou.*")
He would build one shay to beat the taown
'N' the keounty 'n' all the kentry raoun';
It should be so built that it couldn't break daown;
"Fur," said the Deacon, "t's mighty plain
That the weakes' place mus' stan' the strain;
'N' the way t' fix it, uz I maintain, is only jest
T' make that place uz strong uz the rest."

So the Deacon inquired of the village folk
Where he could find the strongest oak,
That couldn't be split nor bent nor broke,—
That was for spokes and floor and sills;
He sent for lancewood to make the thills;
The crossbars were ash, from the straightest trees,
The panels of white-wood, that cuts like cheese,
But lasts like iron for things like these;
The hubs of logs from the "Settler's ellum,"—
Last of its timbers,—they couldn't sell 'em,
Never an axe had seen their chips,
And the wedges flew from between their lips,
Their blunt ends frizzled like celery-tips;
Step and prop-iron, bolt and screw,
Spring, tire, axle, and linchpin too,
Steel of the finest, bright and blue;

Thoroughbrace bison-skin, thick and wide;
Boot, top, dasher, from tough old hide
Found in the pit when the tanner died.
That was the way he "put her through."—
"There!" said the Deacon, "naow she'll dew!"

Do! I tell you, I rather guess
She was a wonder, and nothing less!
Colts grew horses, beards turned gray,
Deacon and deaconess dropped away,
Children and grandchildren—where were they?
But there stood the stout old one-horse shay
As fresh as on Lisbon-earthquake-day!

EIGHTEEN HUNDRED; it came and found
The Deacon's masterpiece strong and sound.
Eighteen hundred increased by ten;—
"Hahnsum kerridge" they called it then.

Eighteen hundred and twenty came;—
Running as usual; much the same.
Thirty and forty at last arrive,
And then came fifty, and FIFTY-FIVE.

Little of all we value here
Wakes on the morn of its hundredth year
Without both feeling and looking queer.
In fact, there's nothing that keeps its youth,
So far as I know, but a tree and truth.
(This is a moral that runs at large;
Take it.—You're welcome.—No extra charge.)

FIRST OF NOVEMBER,—The Earthquake-day
There are traces of age in the one-hoss shay,
A general flavor of mild decay,
But nothing local, as one may say.
There couldn't be,—for the Deacon's art
Had made it so like in every part
That there wasn't a chance for one to start.
For the wheels were just as strong as the thills,
And the floor was just as strong as the sills,
And the panels just as strong as the floor,
And the whipple-tree neither less nor more,
And the back-crossbar as strong as the fore,
And spring and axle and hub *encore*.
And yet, *as a whole*, it is past a doubt,
In another hour it will be *worn out!*

First of November, 'Fifty-five!
This morning the parson takes a drive.
Now, small boys, get out of the way!
Here comes the wonderful one-hoss shay,
Drawn by a rat-tailed, ewe-necked bay.
"Huddup!" said the parson.—Off went they.

The parson was working his Sunday's text,—
Had got to *fifthly*, and stopped perplexed
And what the—Moses—was coming next.
All at once the horse stood still,
Close by the meet'n'-house on the hill.
—First a shiver, and then a thrill,
Then something decidedly like a spill,—
And the parson was sitting upon a rock,
At half past nine by the meet'n'-house clock,—
Just the hour of the Earthquake shock!
—What do you think the parson found,
When he got up and stared around?
The poor old chaise in a heap or mound,
As if it had been to the mill and ground!
You see, of course, if you're not a dunce,
How it went to pieces all at once,—
All at once, and nothing first,—
Just as bubbles do when they burst.

End of the wonderful one-hoss shay.
Logic is logic. That's all I say.

Oliver Wendell Holmes

THE DREAM OF EUGENE ARAM

'Twas in the prime of summer time,
   An evening calm and cool,
And four-and-twenty happy boys
   Came bounding out of school;
There were some that ran, and some that leapt
   Like troutlets in a pool.

Away they sped with gamesome minds
   And souls untouched by sin;
To a level mead they came, and there
   They drove the wickets in:
Pleasantly shone the setting sun
   Over the town of Lynn.

Like sportive deer they coursed about,
   And shouted as they ran,
Turning to mirth all things of earth
   As only boyhood can;
But the usher sat remote from all,
   A melancholy man!

His hat was off, his vest apart,
   To catch heaven's blessèd breeze;
For a burning thought was in his brow,
   And his bosom ill at ease,
So he leaned his head on his hands, and read
   The book between his knees.

Leaf after leaf he turned it o'er,
   Nor ever glanced aside—
For the peace of his soul he read that book
   In the golden eventide;
Much study had made him very lean,
   And pale, and leaden-eyed.

At last he shut the ponderous tome;
　With a fast and fervent grasp
He strained the dusky covers close,
　And fixed the brazen hasp:
"O God! could I so close my mind,
　And clasp it with a clasp!"

Then leaping on his feet upright,
　Some moody turns he took—
Now up the mead, then down the mead,
　And past a shady nook;
And, lo! he saw a little boy
　That pored upon a book.

"My gentle lad, what is 't you read—
　Romance or fairy fable?
Or is it some historic page,
　Of kings and crowns unstable?"
The young boy gave an upward glance—
　"It is 'The Death of Abel.' "

The usher took six hasty strides,
　As smit with sudden pain—
Six hasty strides beyond the place,
　Then slowly back again;
And down he sat beside the lad,
　And talked with him of Cain;

And, long since then, of bloody men,
　Whose deeds tradition saves;
And lonely folk cut off unseen,
　And hid in sudden graves;
And horrid stabs, in groves forlorn;
　And murders done in caves;

And how the sprites of injured men
    Shriek upward from the sod;
Ay, how the ghostly hand will point
    To show the burial-clod;
And unknown facts of guilty acts
    Are seen in dreams from God.

He told how murderers walked the earth
    Beneath the curse of Cain—
With crimson clouds before their eyes,
    And flames about their brain;
For blood has left upon their souls
    Its everlasting stain!

"And well," quoth he, "I know, for truth,
    Their pangs must be extreme—
Woe, woe, unutterable woe!—
    Who spill life's sacred stream!
For why? Methought, last night I wrought
    A murder, in a dream!

"One that had never done me wrong—
    A feeble man and old;
I led him to a lonely field—
    The moon shone clear and cold;
Now here, said I, this man shall die;
    And I will have his gold!

"Two sudden blows with a ragged stick,
    And one with a heavy stone,
One hurried gash with a hasty knife—
    And then the deed was done:
There was nothing lying at my feet
    But lifeless flesh and bone!

"Nothing but lifeless flesh and bone,
    That could not do me ill;
And yet I feared him all the more
    For lying there so still:
There was a manhood in his look
    That murder could not kill!

"And lo! the universal air
    Seemed lit with ghastly flame—
Ten thousand thousand dreadful eyes
    Were looking down in blame;
I took the dead man by his hand,
    And called upon his name.

"O God! it made me quake to see
    Such sense within the slain;
But when I touched the lifeless clay,
    The blood gushed out amain!
For every clot a burning spot
    Was scorching in my brain!

"My head was like an ardent coal,
    My heart as solid ice;
My wretched, wretched soul, I knew,
    Was at the Devil's price:
A dozen times I groaned—the dead
    Had never groaned but twice.

"And now, from forth the frowning sky,
    From the heaven's topmost height,
I heard a voice—the awful voice
    Of the blood-avenging sprite:
'Thou guilty man! take up thy dead,
    And hide it from my sight!'

"I took the dreary body up,
    And cast it in a stream—
The sluggish water black as ink,
    The depth was so extreme:
My gentle boy, remember, this
    Is nothing but a dream!

"Down went the corse with a hollow plunge,
    And vanished in the pool;
Anon I cleansed my bloody hands,
    And washed my forehead cool,
And sat among the urchins young,
    That evening, in the school.

"O Heaven! to think of their white souls,
    And mine so black and grim!
I could not share a childish prayer,
    Nor join in evening hymn;
Like a devil of the pit I seemed,
    'Mid holy cherubim!

"And peace went with them, one and all,
    And each calm pillow spread;
But Guilt was my grim chamberlain,
    That lighted me to bed,
And drew my midnight curtains round
    With fingers bloody red!

"All night I lay in agony,
    In anguish dark and deep;
My fevered eyes I dared not close,
    But stared aghast at Sleep:
For sin had rendered unto her
    The keys of hell to keep!

"All night I lay in agony,
  From weary chime to chime;
With one besetting horrid hint
  That racked me all the time—
A mighty yearning, like the first
  Fierce impulse unto crime—

"One stern tyrannic thought, that made
  All other thoughts its slave!
Stronger and stronger every pulse
  Did that temptation crave—
Still urging me to go and see
  The dead man in his grave!

"Heavily I rose up, as soon
  As light was in the sky,
And sought the black accursèd pool
  With a wild, misgiving eye:
And I saw the dead in the river-bed,
  For the faithless stream was dry.

"Merrily rose the lark, and shook
  The dew-drop from its wing;
But I never marked its morning flight,
  I never heard it sing:
For I was stooping once again
  Under the horrid thing.

"With breathless speed, like a soul in chase,
  I took him up and ran;
There was no time to dig a grave
  Before the day began—
In a lonesome wood, with heaps of leaves,
  I hid the murdered man!

"And all that day I read in school,
  But my thought was otherwhere;
As soon as the midday task was done,
  In secret I was there—
And a mighty wind had swept the leaves,
  And still the corse was bare!

"Then down I cast me on my face,
  And first began to weep,
For I knew my secret then was one
  That earth refused to keep—
Or land or sea, though he should be
  Ten thousand fathoms deep.

"So wills the fierce avenging sprite,
  Till blood for blood atones!
Ay, though he's buried in a cave,
  And trodden down with stones,
And years have rotted off his flesh—
  The world shall see his bones!

"O God! that horrid, horrid dream
  Besets me now awake!
Again—again, with dizzy brain,
  The human life I take;
And my red right hand grows raging hot,
  Like Cranmer's at the stake.

"And still no peace for the restless clay
  Will wave or mold allow;
The horrid thing pursues my soul—
  It stands before me now!"
The fearful boy looked up, and saw
  Huge drops upon his brow.

That very night, while gentle sleep
    The urchin eyelids kissed,
Two stern-faced men set out from Lynn,
    Through the cold and heavy mist;
And Eugene Aram walked between,
    With gyves upon his wrist.

Thomas Hood

BLOW ME EYES!

When I was young and full o' pride,
    A-standin' on the grass
And gazin' o'er the water-side,
    I seen a fisher lass.
"O, fisher lass, be kind awhile,"
    I asks 'er quite unbid.
"Please look into me face and smile"—
    And, blow me eyes, she did!

O, blow me light and blow me blow,
I didn't think she'd charm me so—
  But, blow me eyes, she did!

She seemed so young and beautiful
  I *had* to speak perlite,
(The afternoon was long and dull,
  But she was short and bright.)
"This ain't no place," I says, "to stand—
  Let's take a walk instid,
Each holdin' of the other's hand"—
  And, blow me eyes, she did!

O, blow me light and blow me blow,
I sort o' thunk she wouldn't go—
  But, blow me eyes, she did!

And as we walked along a lane
  With no one else to see,
Me heart was filled with sudden pain,
  And so I says to she:
"If you would have me actions speak
  The words what can't be hid,
You'd sort o' let me kiss yer cheek"—
  And, blow me eyes, she did!

O, blow me light and blow me blow,
How sweet she was I didn't know—
  But, blow me eyes, *she* did!

But pretty soon me shipmate Jim
  Came strollin' down the beach,
And she began a-oglin' him
  As pretty as a peach.
"O, fickle maid o' false intent,"

Impulsively I chid,
"Why don't you go and wed that gent?"
And, blow me eyes, she did!

O, blow me light and blow me blow,
I didn't think she'd treat me so—
But, blow me eyes, she did!
Wallace Irwin

A NAUTICAL EXTRAVAGANZA

I stood one day by the breezy bay
A-watching the ships go by,
When a tired tar said, with a shake of his head:
"I wisht I could tell a lie!

"I've seen some sights as would jigger yer lights
And they've jiggered me own, in sooth,
But I ain't wuth a darn at spinnin' a yarn
What wanders away from the truth.

"We were out in the gig, the Rigagajig,
Jest a mile and a half to sea,
When Capting Snook, with a troubled look,
He came and he says to me:

" 'O Bos'n Smith, make haste forthwith
And hemstitch the fo'ard sail;
Accordion pleat the dory sheet,
For there's going to be a gale!'

"I straightway did as the capting bid—
No sooner the job was through
When the north wind, whoof, bounced over the roof,
And, murderin' lights, she blew!

"She blew the tars right off the spars,
    And the spars right off the mast,
Sails and pails and anchors and nails
    Flew by on the wings o' the blast.

"The galley shook as she blew our cook
    Straight out o' the porthole glim,
While pots and pans, kettles and cans
    Went clatterin' after him.

"She blew the fire from our gallant stove
    And the coal from our gallant bin,
She whistled apace past the capting's face
    And blew the beard off his chin!

" 'O wizzel me dead!' the capting said
    (And the words blew out of his mouth);
'We're lost, I fear, if the wind don't veer
    And blow a while from the south.'

"And wizzel me dead, no sooner he'd said
    Them words that blew from his mouth,
Than the wind switched round with a hurricane sound
    And blew straight in from the south.

"We opened our eyes with a wild surprise,
    And never a word to say—
In changin' her tack the wind blew back
    The things that she'd blew away!

"She blew the tars back onto the spars,
    And the spars back onto the mast;
Back flew the pails, the sails and the nails,
    Which into the ship stuck fast.

"And 'fore we could look she blew back the cook
    Straight into the galley coop,
Back dropped the pans, the kettles and cans,
    Without even spillin' the soup.

"She blew the fire back into the stove
    Where it burnt in its proper place—
And all of us cheered as she blew the beard
    Back on the capting's face.

"There's more o' me tale," said the sailor hale,
    "As would jigger yer lights, in sooth,
But I ain't wuth a darn, at spinnin' a yarn
    What wanders away from the truth."

                                    Wallace Irwin

THE POWERFUL EYES
O' JEREMY TAIT

An old sea-dog on a sailor's log
    Thus spake to a passer-by:
"The most onnatteral thing on earth
    Is the power o' the human eye—
Oh, bless me! yes, oh, blow me! yes—
    It's the power o' the human eye!

"We'd left New York en route for Cork
    A day and a half to sea,
When Jeremy Tait, our fourteenth mate,
    He fastened his eyes on me.

"And wizzle me hook! 'twas a powerful look
    That flashed from them eyes o' his;
I was terrified from heart to hide
    And chilled to me bones and friz.

" 'O Jeremy Tait, O fourteenth mate'
    I hollers with looks askance,
'Full well I wist ye're a hypnotist,
    So please to remove yer glance!'

"But Jeremy laughed as he turned abaft
    His glance like a demon rat,
And he frightened the cook with his piercin' look,
    And he startled the captain's cat.

"Oh, me, oh my! When he turned his eye
    On our very efficient crew,
They fell like dead, or they stood like lead
    And stiff as a poker grew.

"So early and late did Jeremy Tait
    That talent o' his employ,
Which caused the crew, and the captain, too,
    Some moments of great annoy.

"For we loved J. Tait, our fourteenth mate
    As an officer brave and true,
But we quite despised bein' hypnotized
    When we had so much work to do.

"So we grabbed J. Tait, our fourteenth mate
    (His eyes bein' turned away),
By collar and sleeve, and we gave a heave,
    And chucked him into the spray.

"His eyes they flashed as in he splashed,
    But this glance it was sent too late,
For close to our bark a man-eatin' shark
    Jumped after Jeremy Tait.

"And you can bet he would ha' been et
  If he hadn't have did as he done—
Straight at the shark an optical spark
  From his terrible eye he spun.

"Then the shark he shook at Jeremy's look
  And he quailed at Jeremy's glance;
Then he gave a sort of a sharkery snort
  And fell right into a trance!

"Quite mesmerized and hypnotized
  That submarine monster lay;
Meek as a shrimp, with his fins all limp,
  He silently floated away.

"So we all of us cried with a conscious pride,
  'Hurrah for Jeremy Tait!'
And we hove a line down into the brine
  And reskied him from his fate.

"And the captain cries 'We kin use them eyes
  To mighty good purpose soon.
Men, spread the sails—we're a-goin' for whales,
  And we don't need nary harpoon.

" 'For when we hail a blubberous whale
  A-spoutin' the water high,
We'll sail up bold and knock 'im cold
  With the power o' Jeremy's eye!' "

And thus on his log the old sea-dog
  Sat whittling nautical chips:
"Oh, powerf'ler far than the human eye
  Is the truth o' the human lips;
But rarest of all is the pearls that fall
  From a truthful mariner's lips."

Wallace Irwin

LA BELLE DAME SANS MERCI

O what can ail thee, knight-at-arms,
  Alone and palely loitering?
The sedge has wither'd from the lake,
  And no birds sing.

O what can ail thee, knight-at-arms!
  So haggard and so woebegone?
The squirrel's granary is full,
  And the harvest's done.

I see a lily on thy brow
  With anguish moist and fever dew,
And on thy cheeks a fading rose
  Fast withereth too.

I met a lady in the meads,
  Full beautiful—a faery's child,
Her hair was long, her foot was light,
  And her eyes were wild.

I made a garland for her head,
  And bracelets too, and fragrant zone;
She look'd at me as she did love,
  And made sweet moan.

I set her on my pacing steed
  And nothing else saw all day long,
For sidelong would she bend, and sing
  A faery's song.

She found me roots of relish sweet,
  And honey wild and manna dew,
And sure in language strange she said,
  "I love thee true!"

She took me to her elfin grot,
  And there she wept and sigh'd full sore;
And there I shut her wild, wild eyes
  With kisses four.

And there she lullèd me asleep,
  And there I dream'd—Ah! woe betide!
The latest dream I ever dream'd
  On the cold hill's side.

I saw pale kings and princes too,
  Pale warriors, death-pale were they all;
Who cried—"La Belle Dame sans Merci
  Hath thee in thrall!"

I saw their starved lips in the gloam
  With horrid warning gapèd wide,
And I awoke and found me here
  On the cold hill's side.

And this is why I sojourn here
  Alone and palely loitering,
Though the sedge is wither'd from the lake,
  And no birds sing.

                                    John Keats

BRADY'S BEND

This is the story of
The brawny Brady riflemen,
John,
    James,
And the celebrated Samuel—
Who fought Bald Eagle with
The Pennsylvania rifle when
Chief Bald Eagle was
The tomahawk of hell.

Old John Brady was
At Valley Forge and Germantown,
Some
    say,
At the battle of the Brandywine.
He brought a many of
The tomahawking vermin down,
Before they fixed him with
The Indian sign.

Young Jim Brady was
A-harvesting a field in ear,
Long
    gun
Left a-leaning on a stubble stack,
When Chief Bald Eagle like
A weasel come a-eeling near,
And dropped Jim Brady with
A bullet in his back.

Left him lying like
A chicken when its head is chopped,
Scalped
    him
With a whooping-coughing caterwaul.
But sure and as soon as
The shooting and the shouting stopped,
The dead man dying there
Begun to crawl.

Crawled to the river bank
A-hunting for a boat he had
Hid
    there,
Half rotting in the river mud.
For help was afar away,
And forty mile to float he had,
Young Jim Brady with
His head all over blood.

Down the Susquehanna he
Slipped across the river sand,
Wet
    rock
A-shining like a scalping knife.
Sunset, sunrise
Burned upon the river and
Reddened, like his forehead with
The blood of life.

"Tell my brother how
Bald Eagle took my hair away.
Tell
    Sam
To remember, like I told him, to

Trail Bald Eagle like
A beagle over there away,
And lift the scalping lock
The Indians do."

Up the Alleghany where
The Great Chief made his stand,
Sam
    went
A-harrying and hunting him.
Till back by the river bend,
That's named now for Brady's band,
He scalped Bald Eagle like
He promised Jim.

He killed Bald Eagle by
The river Alleghany—a
Great
    Chief—
Did the Samuel, aforesaid,
Who scalped more Indians in
The State of Pennsylvania
Than any other white man
Alive or dead.

This is the story of
The brawny Brady riflemen,
  John,
    James,
And the celebrated Samuel—
Who fought Bald Eagle with
The Pennsylvania rifle when
Chief Bald Eagle was
The tomahawk of hell.
               Martha Keller

THE KNIGHT'S LEAP

A Legend of Altenahr

So the foemen have fired the gate, men of mine;
 And the water is spent and gone?
Then bring me a cup of the red Ahr-wine:
 I never shall drink but this one.

And reach me my harness, and saddle my horse,
 And lead him me round to the door:
He must take such a leap tonight perforce,
 As horse never took before.

I have fought my fight, I have lived my life,
 I have drunk my share of wine;
From Trier to Coln there was never a knight
 Led a merrier life than mine.

I have lived by the saddle for years two score;
 And if I must die on tree,
Then the old saddle-tree, which has borne me of yore,
 Is the properest timber for me.

So now to show Bishop, and burgher, and priest,
    How the Altenahr hawk can die;
If they smoke the old falcon out of his nest,
    He must take to his wings and fly!

He harnessed himself by the clear moonshine,
    And he mounted his horse at the door;
And he drained such a cup of the red Ahr-wine,
    As man never drained before.

He spurred the old horse, and he held him tight,
    And he leapt him out over the wall;
Out over the cliff, out into the night,
    Three hundred feet of fall.

They found him next morning below in the glen,
    With never a bone in him whole—
A mass or a prayer, now, good gentlemen,
    For such a bold rider's soul.

                              Charles Kingsley

THE STORY OF SAMUEL JACKSON

I'll tell you of a sailor now, a tale that can't be beat,
His name was Samuel Jackson, and his height was seven
    feet;
And how this man was shipwrecked in the far Pacific Isles,
And of the heathen natives with their suppositious wiles.

Now when the others cut the ship, because she was a
    wreck,
They left this Samuel Jackson there, a-standin' on the
    deck—
That is, a standin' on the deck, while sittin' on the boom;
They wouldn't let him in the boat 'cos he took up too much
    room.

When up there came a tilted wave, and like a horse it
    romped,
It fell like mountains on the boat, and so the boat was
    swamped;
And of those selfish mariners full every one was drowned,
While Samuel, standing on the deck, beheld it safe and
    sound.

Now when the sea grew soft and still, and all the gale was
    o'er.
Sam Jackson made himself a raft, and paddled safe ashore.
For fear of fatal accidents—not knowin' what might come,
He took a gun and matches, with a prudent cask of rum.

Now this island where he landed proved as merry as a fife,
For its indigents he'd ne'er beheld a white man in their life;
Such incidents as rum and guns they never yet had seen,
And likewise, in religion, they were awful jolly green.

But they had a dim tradition, from their ancestors, in
    course,
Which they had somehow *de*rived from a very ancient
    source:
How that a god would come to them, and set the island
    right;
And how he should be orful tall, and likewise pearly white.

Now when they saw this Samuel approachin' on his raft,
The news through all the island shades was quickly tele-
    graft,
How all their tribulat-i-ons would speedily be past,
'Cos the long-expected sucker was invadin' 'em at last.

Now when Sam Jackson stept ashore, as modest as you
    please,
Nine thousand bloomin' savages received him on their
    knees;
He looked around in wonderment, regardin' it as odd,
Not bein' much accustomed to be worshipped as a god.

But he twigged the situation, and with a pleasin' smile
Stretched out his hands, a-blessin' all the natives of the isle;
He did it well, although his paws were bigger than a pan,
Because he was habitual a most politeful man.

So to return their manners, and nary-wise for fun,
He raised himself with dignity, and then fired off his gun:
So all allowed that he must be one of the heavenly chaps,
Since he went about with lightning and dispensed with
    thunderclaps.

They took him on their shoulders, and he let it go for good,
And went into their city in the which a temple stood,
And sot him on the altar, and made him their salams,
And brought him pleasant coco-nuts, with chickens, po
    and yams.

And from that day henceforward, in a captivating style,
He relegated, as he pleased, the natives of that isle;
And when an unbeliever rose—as now and then were
     some,
He cured their irreligion with a little taste of rum.

He settled all their business, and he did it very well,
So everything went booming like a blessed wedding bell;
Eleven lovely feminines attended to his wants,
And a guard of honour followed him to all his usual haunts.

Now what mortal men are made of, that they can't put up
     with bliss,
I do not know, but this I know, that Sam got tired of this;
He wished that he was far away, again aboard a ship,
And all he thought of—night and day—was givin' 'em the
     slip.

And so one night when all was still and every soul asleep,
He got into a good canoe and paddled o'er the deep,
But oh the row the natives made, when early in the morn
They came to worship Samuel, and found their god was
     gone!

Then Samuel travelled many days, but had the luck at last
To meet a brig from Boston where he shipped before the
     mast;
And he gave it as his sentiments, and no one thought it
     odd,
He was better off as sailor than when sailing as a god.

Now many years had flown away when Samuel was forgot,
There came a ship for pearl shell unto that lonely spot;
They went into the temple, and what do you suppose
They found the natives worshipping—a suit of Samuel's
     clothes!

And this was the tradition of the people of the soil,
How once a great divinity had ruled upon their isle;
Four fathoms tall, with eyes like fire, and such was their
    believin',
One night he got upon the moon—and sailed away to
    Heaven!

Charles Godfrey Leland

THE CAULKER

A Fish Story

("A whaler whose plates had been pierced was saved
by a large fish which was drawn into the hole by the
inrush of water and got jammed there. The fish only
became dislodged when they were nearly in port."
—*Daily Paper.*)

A strong imagination from my youth has been combined
With insatiate love of detail and a quick inquiring mind;
I have therefore made an effort at discovering what are
The actual facts that lie behind this interesting par.

It was the whaler *Whatshername*—I'm not allowed to
    state
The tonnage, destination, nationality or date—
But anyway a rock (or wreck) nigh brought her to her
    doom
And made a most impressive hole abaft the engine-room.

The hole was very large indeed; at once the water rolled
Unhindered through the orifice and swamped the after-
    hold;
And very soon, unless the crew could reach a port and
    dock her,
The whole concern would go for good to Davy Jones's
    locker.

All hands were piped to man the pumps, and manfully
    they pumped,
While feverishly up and down the bridge the skipper
    stumped;
But stumped the "Old Man" ne'er so fast nor pumped the
    men so hard,
The water in the after-hold was gaining yard by yard.

"We're lost!" the captain cried. "That's so," the mate he
    made reply.
"Then man the boats," the skipper said, a tear in either
    eye;
But scarcely had he wiped them off and dried them on his
    trouser
When a sailor ran and cried, "The pumps are gaining now,
    Sir."

Yes, fate had acted in a way as kind as it was odd;
In point of actual fact, some fish—a conger or a cod,
A whale or shark (though which it was I really mustn't
    say)—
Drawn by the inrush through the hole, had stuck and
    blocked the way.

This for the moment saved the crew from quite a pretty
    pickle,
For now the flood that raged before became the merest
    trickle.
"Then pump again!" the captain cried. The mate re-
    marked, "Ay, ay!"
And very soon the after-hold was practically dry.

"Full steam ahead!" the skipper said. "Make for the nearest
    land!"
"Ay, ay, Sir," said the mate—when up there rushed a
    fo'c's'le hand.

"Excusing me the liberty o' speakin', Sir," he said,
"They've pumped the blinkin' 'old so dry the bung'll soon
      be dead."

"Why not, my man?" the captain cried. The mate re-
      echoed, "Why?"
The man replied, "It don't seem fair ter let the creetur
      die;
But quite apart from gratitood I've 'eard it said, I think,
That fish wot die will quickly dry, and then o' course
      they shrink."

"The deuce they do!" the captain cried. The mate said,
      "Gad, he's right!
The sea will push him in unless we keep her watertight."
"Go, fill the biggest pail we've got," the ingenious skipper
      said,
"With water to the brim and hold it round the fish's head."

Then straight that seaman hurries to the water-cask and
      fills
The largest pail with water and he holds it round his gills;
But even then, although the stuff did cheer him up a bit,
It still was clear that kindly fish felt very far from fit.

The captain watched with twitching lips; the mate began
      to curse;
The fish was shrinking rapidly, it fitted worse and worse;
The water poured in tons aboard; the fish still shrank and
      shrank,
Until at last it slipped right in, and then the good ship
      sank.

The shore was near; the crew were saved and reached
      their native land;
But still the skipper and the mate can never understand
Exactly why a fish should die with water round its head.

"We can't have *drowned* it?" asked the mate. "Why, no,"
    the skipper said.

But in the crew was one who knew and sadly slunk
    away—
His conscience needs must trouble him until his dying
    day—
The fo'c's'le hand. "My fault!" he groans. "It's all my silly
    fault;
I gave the brute *fresh* water, when of course he wanted
    salt."

M. A. Lewis

THE BLACKSMITH'S SERENADE

John Littlehouse the redhead was a large ruddy man
Quite proud to be a blacksmith, and he loved Polly Ann,
    Polly Ann.
Straightway to her window with his iron guitar he came
Breathing like a blacksmith—his wonderful heart's flame.
Though not very bashful and not very bold
He had reached the plain conclusion his passion must be
    told.
And so he sang: "Awake, awake,"—this hip-hoo-ray-ious
    man.
"Do you like me, do you love me, Polly Ann, Polly Ann?
The rooster on my coalshed crows at break of day.
It makes a person happy to hear his roundelay.
The fido in my woodshed barks at fall of night.
He makes one feel so safe and snug. He barks exactly
    right.
I swear to do my stylish best and purchase all I can
Of the flummeries, flunkeries and mummeries of man.

And I will carry in the coal and the water from the spring
And I will sweep the porches if you will cook and sing.
No doubt your Pa sleeps like a rock. Of course Ma is
    awake
But dares not say she hears me, for gentle custom's sake.
Your sleeping father knows I am a decent honest man.
Will you wake him, Polly Ann,
And if he dares deny it I will thrash him, lash bash mash
Hash him, Polly Ann.
Hum hum hum, fee fie fo fum—
And my brawn should wed your beauty.
Do you hear me, Polly Ann, Polly Ann?"

Polly had not heard of him before, but heard him now.
She blushed behind the shutters like a pippin on the
    bough.
She was not overfluttered, she was not overbold.
She was glad a lad was living with a passion to be told.
But she spoke up to her mother: "Oh, what an awful
    man:—"
This merry merry quite contrary tricky trixy, Polly Ann,
    Polly Ann.
The neighbors put their heads out of the windows. They
    said:—
"What sort of turtle dove is this that seems to wake the
    dead?"
Yes, in their nighties whispered this question to the night.
They did not dare to shout it. It wouldn't be right.
And so, I say, they whispered:—"Does she hear this awful
    man,
Polly Ann, Polly Ann?"

John Littlehouse the redhead sang on of his desires:
"Steel makes the wires of lyres, makes the frames of
    terrible towers
And circus chariots' tires.

Believe me, dear, a blacksmith man can feel.
I will bind you, if I can to my ribs with hoops of steel.
Do you hear me, Polly Ann, Polly Ann?"

And then his tune was silence, for he was not a fool.
He let his voice rest, his iron guitar cool.
And thus he let the wind sing, the stars sing and the grass
    sing,
The prankishness of love sing, the girl's tingling feet
    sing,
Her trembling sweet hands sing, her mirror in the dark
    sing,
Her grace in the dark sing, her pillow in the dark sing,
The savage in her blood sing, her starved little heart sing,
Silently sing.

"Yes, I hear you, Mister Man,"
To herself said Polly Ann, Polly Ann.

He shouted one great loud *"Good night,"* and laughed,
And skipped home.
And every star was winking in the wide wicked dome.
And early in the morning, sweet Polly stole away.
And though the town went crazy, she is his wife today.

Vachel Lindsay

THE LUCK OF EDENHALL

Of Edenhall, the youthful Lord
Bids sound the festal trumpet's call.
He rises at the banquet board,
And cries, 'mid the drunken revellers all,
"Now bring me the Luck of Edenhall!"

The butler hears the words with pain,
The house's oldest seneschal,
Takes slow from its silken cloth again
The drinking glass of crystal tall;
They call it the Luck of Edenhall.

Then said the Lord, "This glass to praise,
Fill with red wine from Portugal!"
The gray-beard with trembling hand obeys;
A purple light shines over all,
It beams from the Luck of Edenhall.

Then speaks the Lord, and waves it light,
"This glass of flashing crystal tall
Gave to my sires the Fountain-Sprite;
She wrote in it, *If this glass doth fall,*
Farewell then, O Luck of Edenhall!

" 'Twas right a goblet the Fate should be
Of the joyous race of Edenhall!
Deep draughts drink we right willingly;
And willingly ring, with merry call,
Kling! klang! to the Luck of Edenhall!"

First rings it deep, and full, and mild,
Like to the song of a nightingale;
Then like the roar of a torrent wild;
Then mutters at last like the thunder's fall,
The glorious Luck of Edenhall.

"For its keeper takes a race of might,
The fragile goblet of crystal tall;
It has lasted longer than is right;
Kling! klang!—with a harder blow than all
Will I try the Luck of Edenhall!"

As the goblet ringing flies apart,
Suddenly cracks the vaulted hall;
And through the rift, the wild flames start;
The guests in dust are scattered all,
With the breaking Luck of Edenhall!

In storms the foe, with fire and sword;
He in the night had scaled the wall,
Slain by the sword lies the youthful Lord,
But holds in his hand the crystal tall,
The shattered Luck of Edenhall.

On the morrow the butler gropes alone,
The gray-beard in the desert hall,
He seeks his Lord's burnt skeleton,
He seeks in the dismal ruin's fall
The shards of the Luck of Edenhall.

"The stone wall," saith he, "doth fall aside,
Down must the stately columns fall;
Glass is this earth's Luck and Pride;
In atoms shall fall this earthy ball
One day like the Luck of Edenhall!"

Henry Wadsworth Longfellow

PAUL REVERE'S RIDE

Listen, my children, and you shall hear
Of the midnight ride of Paul Revere,
On the eighteenth of April, in Seventy-five;
Hardly a man is now alive.
Who remembers that famous day and year.

He said to his friend, "If the British march
By land or sea from the town to-night,
Hang a lantern aloft in the belfry arch
Of the North Church tower as a signal light,—
One, if by land, and two, if by sea;
And I on the opposite shore will be,
Ready to ride and spread the alarm
Through every Middlesex village and farm,
For the country folk to be up and to arm."
Then he said "Good-night," and with muffled oar
Silently row'd to the Charlestown shore,
Just as the moon rose over the bay,
Where swinging wide at her moorings lay
The Somerset, British man-of-war;
A phantom ship, with each mast and spar
Across the moon like a prison bar,
And a huge black hulk, that was magnified
By its own reflection in the tide.

Meanwhile his friend, through alley and street,
Wanders and watches with eager ears,
Till in the silence around him he hears
The muster of men at the barrack-door,
The sound of arms, and the tramp of feet,
And the measured tread of the grenadiers
Marching down to their boats on the shore.
Then he climb'd the tower of the Old North Church,
By the wooden stairs, with stealthy tread,
To the belfry-chamber overhead,
And startled the pigeons from their perch
On the sombre rafters, that round him made
Masses of moving shapes of shade,—
By the trembling ladder, steep and tall,
To the highest window in the wall,

Where he paused to listen and look down
A moment on the roofs of the town,
And the moonlight flowing over all.

Beneath, in the churchyard, lay the dead,
In their night-encampment on the hill,
Wrapp'd in silence so deep and still
That he could hear, like a sentinel's tread,
The watchful night-wind, as it went
Creeping along from tent to tent,
And seeming to whisper, "All is well!"
A moment only he feels the spell
Of the place and the hour, and the secret dread
Of the lonely belfry and the dead;
For suddenly all his thoughts are bent
On a shadowy something far away,
Where the river widens to meet the bay,
A line of black that bends and floats
On the rising tide like a bridge of boats.

Meanwhile, impatient to mount and ride,
Booted and spurr'd, with a heavy stride
On the opposite shore walk'd Paul Revere.
Now he patted his horse's side,
Now he gazed at the landscape far and near,
Then, impetuous, stamp'd the earth,
And turn'd and tighten'd his saddle-girth;
But mostly he watch'd with eager search
The belfry-tower of the Old North Church,
As it rose above the graves on the hill,
Lonely and spectral and sombre and still.
And lo! as he looks, on the belfry's height
A glimmer, and then a gleam of light!
He springs to the saddle, the bridle he turns,
But lingers and gazes, till full on his sight
A second lamp in the belfry burns.

A hurry of hoofs in a village street,
A shape in the moonlight, a bulk in the dark,
And beneath, from the pebbles, in passing, a spark
Struck out by a steed flying fearless and fleet:
That was all; and yet, through the gloom and the light,
The fate of a nation was riding that night;
And the spark struck out by that steed in his flight
Kindled the land into flame with its heat.

He had left the village and mounted the steep,
And beneath him, tranquil and broad and deep,
Is the Mystic, meeting the ocean tides,
And under the alders that skirt its edge,
Now soft on the sand, now loud on the ledge,
Is heard the tramp of his steed as he rides.

It was twelve by the village clock
When he crossed the bridge into Medford town.
He heard the crowing of the cock,
And the barking of the farmer's dog,
And felt the damp of the river fog,
That rises after the sun goes down.

It was one by the village clock
When he galloped into Lexington.
He saw the gilded weathercock
Swim in the moonlight as he pass'd,
And the meeting-house windows, blank and bare,
Gaze at him with a spectral glare,
As if they already stood aghast
At the bloody work they would look upon.

It was two by the village clock
When he came to the bridge in Concord town.
He heard the bleating of the flock,

And the twitter of birds among the trees,
And felt the breath of the morning breeze
Blowing over the meadows brown.
And one was safe and asleep in his bed
Who at the bridge would be first to fall,
Who that day would be lying dead,
Pierced by a British musket-ball.

You know the rest; in the books you have read,
How the British regulars fired and fled,—
How the farmers gave them ball for ball,
From behind each fence and farmyard wall,
Chasing the red-coats down the lane,
Then crossing the fields to emerge again
Under the trees at the turn of the road,
And only pausing to fire and load.

So through the night rode Paul Revere,
And so through the night went his cry of alarm
To every Middlesex village and farm,—
A cry of defiance, and not of fear,
A voice in the darkness, a knock at the door,
And a word that shall echo forevermore!
For, borne on the night-wind of the Past,
Through all our history, to the last,
In the hour of darkness, and peril, and need,
The people will waken and listen to hear
The hurrying hoof-beats of that steed,
And the midnight message of Paul Revere.

Henry Wadsworth Longfellow

PADDY O'RAFTHER

Paddy, in want of a dinner one day,
Credit all gone, and no money to pay,
Stole from a priest a fat pullet, they say,
   And went to confession just afther;
"Your riv'rince," says Paddy, "I stole this fat hen."
"What, what!" says the priest, "at your ould thricks again?
Faith, you'd rather be staalin' than sayin' *amen*,
              Paddy O'Rafther!"

"Sure, you wouldn't be angry," says Pat, "if you knew
That the best of intintions I had in my view—
For I stole it to make it a present to you,
   And you can absolve me afther."
"Do you think," says the priest, "I'd partake of your theft?
Of your seven small senses you must be bereft—
You're the biggest blackguard that I know, right and left,
              Paddy O'Rafther."

"Then what shall I do with the pullet," says Pat,
"If your riv'rince won't take it? By this and by that
I don't know no more than a dog or a cat
   What your riv'rince would have me be afther."
"Why, then," says his rev'rence, "you sin-blinded owl,
Give back to the man that you stole from his fowl:
For if you do not, 'twill be worse for your sowl,
              Paddy O'Rafther."

Says Paddy, "I ask'd him to take it—'tis thrue
As this minit I'm talkin', your riv'rince, to you;
But he wouldn't resaive it—so what can I do?"
   Says Paddy, nigh choken with laughter.
"By my throth," says the priest, "but the case is absthruse;
If he won't take his hen, why the man is a goose:
'Tis not the first time my advice was no use,
              Paddy O'Rafther."

"But, for sake of your sowl, I would sthrongly advise
To some one in want you would give your supplies—
Some widow, or orphan, with tears in their eyes;
   And *then* you may come to *me* afther."
So Paddy went off to the brisk Widow Hoy.
And the pullet between them was eaten with joy,
And, says she, " 'Pon my word you're the cleverest boy,
                         Paddy O'Rafther."

Then Paddy went back to the priest the next day,
And told him the fowl he had given away
To a poor lonely widow, in want and dismay,
   The loss of her spouse weeping afther.
"Well, now," says the priest, "I'll absolve you, my lad,
For repentantly making the best of the bad,
In feeding the hungry and cheering the sad,
                         Paddy O'Rafther!"
                              Samuel Lover

THE RELIEF OF LUCKNOW

Oh, that last day in Lucknow fort!
   We knew that it was the last;
That the enemy's lines crept surely on,
   And the end was coming fast.

To yield to that foe meant worse than death;
   And the men and we all worked on;
It was one day more of smoke and roar,
   And then it would all be done.

There was one of us, a corporal's wife,
   A fair, young gentle thing,
Wasted with fever in the siege,
   And her mind was wandering.

She lay on the ground, in her Scottish plaid,
  And I took her head on my knee;
"When my father comes hame frae the pleugh," she said,
  "Oh! then please wauken me."

She slept like a child on her father's floor,
  In the flecking of woodbine-shade,
When the house-dog sprawls by the open door,
  And the mother's wheel is stayed.

It was smoke and roar and powder-stench,
  And hopeless waiting for death;
And the soldier's wife, like a full-tired child,
  Seemed scarce to draw her breath.

I sank to sleep; and I had my dream
  Of an English village-lane,
And wall and garden;—but one wild scream
  Brought me back to the roar again.

There Jessie Brown stood listening
  Till a sudden gladness broke
All over her face; and she caught my hand
  And drew me near as she spoke:—

"The Hielanders! O! dinna ye hear
  The slogan far awa'?
The McGregor's. O! I ken it weel;
  It's the grandest o' them a'!

"God bless the bonny Hielanders!
  We're saved! we're saved!" she cried;
And fell on her knees; and thanks to God
  Flowed forth like a full flood-tide.

Along the battery-line her cry
    Had fallen among the men,
And they started back;—they were there to die;
    But was life so near them, then?

They listened for life; the rattling fire
    Far off, and the far-off roar,
Were all; and the colonel shook his head,
    And they turned to their guns once more.

But Jessie said, "The slogan's done;
  But winna ye hear it noo.
The Campbells are comin'? It's no a dream;
  Our succors hae broken through!"

We heard the roar and the rattle afar,
  But the pipes we could not hear;
So the men plied their work of hopeless war,
  And knew that the end was near.

It was not long ere it made its way,—
  A thrilling, ceaseless sound:
It was no noise from the strife afar,
  Or the sappers underground.

It *was* the pipes of the Highlanders!
  And now they played *Auld Lang Syne*,
It came to our men like the voice of God,
  And they shouted along the line.

And they wept, and shook one another's hands,
  And the women sobbed in a crowd;
And every one knelt down where he stood,
  And we all thanked God aloud.

That happy time, when we welcomed them,
  Our men put Jessie first;
And the general gave her his hand, and cheers
  Like a storm from the soldiers burst.

And the pipers' ribbons and tartans streamed,
  Marching round and round our line;
And our joyful cheers were broken with tears,
  As the pipes played *Auld Lang Syne*.

Robert Lowell

small talk

i went into the flea circus
on broadway the other day
and heard a lot of fleas
talking and bragging to each other
one flea had been over to the swell dog show
and was boasting that he had bit
a high priced thoroughbred dog
yeah says another flea
that is nothing to get so proud of
a thoroughbred dog tastes just like a mongrel
i should think you would be more democratic
than to brag about that
go and get a reputation
said a third flea
i went into a circus last spring and bit a lion
i completely conquered him
i made him whine and cringe
he did not bite me back
get out of my way
i am the flea that licked a lion
i said to myself probably
that lion didnt even know he had been bitten
some insects are just like human beings
small talk i said to myself
and went away from there

        archy the cockroach

Don Marquis

[133]

the flattered lightning bug

a lightning bug got
in here the other night a
regular hick from
the real country he was
awful proud of himself you
city insects may think
you are some punkins
but i don t see any
of you flashing in the dark
like we do in
the country all right go
to it says i mehitabel the
cat and that green
spider who lives in your locker
and two or three cockroach
friends of mine and a
friendly rat all gathered
around him and urged him on
and he lightened and
lightened and lightened you
don t see anything like this
in town often he says go to it
we told him it s a
real treat to us and
we nicknamed him broadway
which pleased him
this is the life
he said all i
need is a harbor
under me to be a
statue of liberty and
he got so vain of
himself i had to take

him down a peg you ve
made lightning for two hours
little bug i told him
but i don t hear
any claps of thunder
yet there are some men
like that when he wore
himself out mehitabel
the cat ate him

archy

Don Marquis

THE OLD NAVY

The captain stood on the carronade: "First lieutenant,"
    says he,
"Send all my merry men aft here, for they must list to me;
I haven't the gift of the gab, my sons—because I'm bred
    to the sea;
That ship there is a Frenchman, who means to fight with
    we.
    And odds bobs, hammer and tongs, long as I've been
      to sea,
    I've fought 'gainst every odds—but I've gained the
      victory!

"That ship there is a Frenchman, and if we don't take she,
'Tis a thousand bullets to one, that she will capture we;
I haven't the gift of the gab, my boys; so each man to
    his gun;
If she's not mine in half an hour, I'll flog each mother's
    son.

For odds bobs, hammer and tongs, long as I've been
  to sea,
I've fought 'gainst every odds—and I've gained the
  victory!"

We fought for twenty minutes, when the Frenchman had
  enough;
"I little thought," said he, "that your men were of such
  stuff."
Our captain took the Frenchman's sword, a low bow
  made to he;
"I haven't the gift of the gab, monsieur, but polite I wish
  to be.
  And odds bobs, hammer and tongs, long as I've been
    to sea,
  I've fought 'gainst every odds—and I've gained the
    victory!"

Our captain sent for all of us: "My merry men," said
  he,
"I haven't the gift of the gab, my lads, but yet I thankful
  be;
You've done your duty handsomely, each man stood to
  his gun;
If you hadn't, you villians, as sure as day, I'd have flogged
  each mother's son,
  For odds bobs, hammer and tongs, as long as I'm at
    sea,
  I'll fight 'gainst every odds—and I'll gain the victory!"

Frederick Marryat

CAPE HORN GOSPEL—I

"I was in a hooker once," said Karlssen,
"And Bill, as was a seaman, died,
So we lashed him in an old tarpaulin
And tumbled him across the side;
And the fun of it was that all his gear was
Divided up among the crew
Before that blushing human error,
Our crawling little captain, knew.

"On the passage home one morning
(As certain as I prays for grace)
There was old Bill's shadder a-hauling
At the weather mizzen-topsail brace.
He was all grown green with sea-weed,
He was all lashed up and shored;
So I says to him, I says, 'Why, Billy!
What's a-bringin' of you back aboard?'

" 'I'm a-weary of them there mermaids,'
Says old Bill's ghost to me;
'It ain't no place for a Christian
Below there—under sea.
For it's all blown sand and shipwrecks,
And old bones eaten bare,
And them cold fishy females
With long green weeds for hair.' "

John Masefield

[137]

THE YARN OF THE
LOCH ACHRAY

The *Loch Achray* was a clipper tall
With seven-and-twenty hands in all.
Twenty to hand and reef and haul,
A skipper to sail and mates to bawl
"Tally on to the tackle-fall,
Heave now 'n' start her, heave 'n' pawl!"
    Hear the yarn of a sailor,
    An old yarn learned at sea.

Her crew were shipped and they said "Farewell,
So-long, my Tottie, my lovely gell;
We sail to-day if we fetch to hell,
It's time we tackled the wheel a spell."
    Hear the yarn of a sailor,
    An old yarn learned at sea.

The dockside loafers talked on the quay
The day that she towed down to sea:
"Lord, what a handsome ship she be!
Cheer her, sonny boys, three times three!"
And the dockside loafers gave her a shout
As the red-funnelled tug-boat towed her out;
They gave her a cheer as the custom is,
And the crew yelled "Take our loves to Liz—
Three cheers, bullies, for old Pier Head
'N' the bloody stay-at-homes!" they said.
    Hear the yarn of a sailor,
    An old yarn learned at sea.

In the grey of the coming on of night
She dropped the tug at the Tuskar Light,
'N' the topsails went to the topmast head
To a chorus that fairly awoke the dead.

She trimmed her yards and slanted South
With her royals set and a bone in her mouth.
    Hear the yarn of a sailor,
    An old yarn learned at sea.

She crossed the Line and all went well,
They ate, they slept, and they struck the bell
And I give you a gospel truth when I state
The crowd didn't find any fault with the Mate,
But one night off of the River Plate.
    Hear the yarn of a sailor,
    An old yarn learned at sea.

It freshened up till it blew like thunder
And burrowed her deep lee-scuppers under.
The old man said, "I mean to hang on
Till her canvas busts or her sticks are gone"—
Which the blushing looney did, till at last
Overboard went her mizzen-mast.
    Hear the yarn of a sailor,
    An old yarn learned at sea.

Then a fierce squall struck the *Loch Achray*
And bowed her down to her water-way;
Her main-shrouds gave and her forestay,
And a green sea carried her wheel away;
Ere the watch below had time to dress
She was cluttered up in a blushing mess.
    Hear the yarn of a sailor,
    An old yarn learned at sea.

She couldn't lay-to nor yet pay-off,
And she got swept clean in the bloody trough;
Her masts were gone, and afore you knowed
She filled by the head and down she goed.

Her crew made seven-and-twenty dishes
For the big jack-sharks and the little fishes,
And over their bones the water swishes.
    Hear the yarn of a sailor,
    An old yarn learned at sea.

The wives and girls they watch in the rain
For a ship as won't come home again.
"I reckon it's them head-winds," they say,
"She'll be home to-morrow, if not to-day.
I'll just nip home 'n' I'll air the sheets
'N' buy the fixins 'n' cook the meats
As my man likes 'n' as my man eats."

So home they goes by the windy streets,
Thinking their men are homeward bound
With anchors hungry for English ground,
And the bloody fun of it is, they're drowned!
    Hear the yarn of a sailor,
    An old yarn learned at sea.

John Masefield

THE BALLAD OF THE
HARP-WEAVER

"Son," said my mother,
    When I was knee-high,
"You've need of clothes to cover you,
    And not a rag have I.

"There's nothing in the house
    To make a boy breeches,
Nor shears to cut a cloth with
    Nor thread to take stitches.

[140]

"There's nothing in the house
    But a loaf-end of rye,
And a harp with a woman's head
    Nobody will buy,"
And she began to cry.

That was in the early fall.
    When came the late fall,
"Son," she said, "the sight of you
    Makes your mother's blood crawl,—

"Little skinny shoulder-blades
    Sticking through your clothes!
And where you'll get a jacket from
    God above knows.

"It's lucky for me, lad,
    Your daddy's in the ground,
And can't see the way I let
    His son go around!"
And she made a queer sound.

That was in the late fall.
    When the winter came,
I'd not a pair of breeches
    Nor a shirt to my name.

I couldn't go to school,
    Or out of doors to play.
And all the other little boys
    Passed our way.

"Son," said my mother,
    "Come, climb into my lap,
And I'll chafe your little bones
    While you take a nap."

And, oh, but we were silly
  For half an hour or more,
Me with my long legs
  Dragging on the floor,

A-rock-rock-rocking
  To a mother-goose rhyme!
Oh, but we were happy
  For a half an hour's time!

But there was I, a great boy,
  And what would folks say
To hear my mother singing me
  To sleep all day,
  In such a daft way?

Men say the winter
  Was bad that year;
Fuel was scarce,
  And food was dear.

A wind with a wolf's head
  Howled about our door,
And we burned up the chairs
  And sat upon the floor.

All that was left us
  Was a chair we couldn't break,
And the harp with a woman's head
  Nobody would take,
  For song or pity's sake.

The night before Christmas
  I cried with the cold,
I cried myself to sleep
  Like a two-year-old.

And in the deep night
  I felt my mother rise,
And stare down upon me
  With love in her eyes.

I saw my mother sitting
  On the one good chair,
A light falling on her
  From I couldn't tell where,

Looking nineteen,
  And not a day older,
And the harp with a woman's head
  Leaned against her shoulder.

Her thin fingers, moving
  In the thin, tall strings,
Were weav-weav-weaving
  Wonderful things.

Many bright threads,
  From where I couldn't see,
Were running through the harp-strings
  Rapidly,

And gold threads whistling
  Through my mother's hand,
I saw the web grow,
  And the pattern expand.

She wove a child's jacket,
  And when it was done
She laid it on the floor
  And wove another one.

She wove a red cloak
  So regal to see,
"She's made it for a king's son,"
  I said, "and not for me."
But I knew it was for me.

She wove a pair of breeches
  Quicker than that!
She wove a pair of boots
  And a little cocked hat.

She wove a pair of mittens,
  She wove a little blouse,
She wove all night
  In the still, cold house.

She sang as she worked,
  And the harp-strings spoke;
Her voice never faltered,
  And the thread never broke.
  And when I awoke,—

There sat my mother
  With the harp against her shoulder,
Looking nineteen,
  And not a day older,

A smile about her lips,
  And a light about her head,
And her hands in the harp-strings
  Frozen dead.

And piled up beside her
  And toppling to the skies,
Were the clothes of a king's son,
  Just my size.

                    Edna St. Vincent Millay

THE BOY WHO LAUGHED
AT SANTA CLAUS

In Baltimore there lived a boy.
He wasn't anybody's joy.
Although his name was Jabez Dawes,
His character was full of flaws.
In school he never led his classes,
He hid old ladies' reading glasses,
His mouth was open when he chewed,
And elbows to the table glued.

He stole the milk of hungry kittens,
And walked through doors marked No ADMITTANCE.
He said he acted thus because
There wasn't any Santa Claus.
Another trick that tickled Jabez
Was crying "Boo!" at little babies.
He brushed his teeth, they said in town,
Sideways instead of up and down.

Yet people pardoned every sin,
And viewed his antics with a grin,
Till they were told by Jabez Dawes,
"There isn't any Santa Claus!"
Deploring how he did behave,
His parents swiftly sought their grave.
They hurried through the portals pearly,
And Jabez left the funeral early.

Like whooping cough, from child to child,
He sped to spread the rumor wild:
"Sure as my name is Jabez Dawes
There isn't any Santa Claus!"

Slunk like a weasel or a marten
Through nursery and kindergarten,
Whispering low to every tot,
"There isn't any, no there's not!"

The children wept all Christmas Eve
And Jabez chortled up his sleeve.
No infant dared hang up his stocking
For fear of Jabez' ribald mocking.
He sprawled on his untidy bed,
Fresh malice dancing in his head,
When presently with scalp a-tingling,
Jabez heard a distant jingling;
He heard the crunch of sleigh and hoof
Crisply alighting on the roof.

What good to rise and bar the door?
A shower of soot was on the floor.
What was beheld by Jabez Dawes?
The fireplace full of Santa Claus!
Then Jabez fell upon his knees
With cries of "Don't," and "Pretty please."
He howled, "I don't know where you read it,
But anyhow, I never said it!"

"Jabez," replied the angry saint,
"It isn't I, it's you that ain't.
Although there is a Santa Claus,
There isn't any Jabez Dawes!"
Said Jabez then with impudent vim,
"Oh, yes there is; and I am him!
Your magic don't scare me, it doesn't"—
And suddenly he found he wasn't!

From grimy feet to unkempt locks
Jabez became a jack-in-the-box,
An ugly, vastly ghastly jack
In Santa Claus's bulging pack.
The neighbors heard his mournful squeal;
They searched for him, but not with zeal.
No trace was found of Jabez Dawes,
Which led to thunderous applause,
And people drank a loving cup
And went and hung their stockings up.

All you who sneer at Santa Claus,
Beware the fate of Jabez Dawes,
The saucy boy who mocked the saint.
Donder and Blitzen licked off his paint.

Ogden Nash

FORTY SINGING SEAMEN*

Across the seas of Wonderland to Mogadore we plodded,
Forty singing seamen in an old black barque,
And we landed in the twilight where a Polyphemus
    nodded,
With his battered moon-eye winking red and yellow
    through the dark!
  For his eye was growing mellow,
  Rich and ripe and red and yellow,
As was time, since old Ulysses made him bellow in the
    dark!
Since Ulysses bunged his eye up with a pine-torch in the
    dark!

* From *Collected Poems*, Volume I, by Alfred Noyes, Copyright,
1906, 1934, by Alfred Noyes. Published by J. B. Lippincott Company.

Were they mountains in the gloaming or the giant's ugly
  shoulders
Just beneath the rolling eye-ball, with its bleared and
  vinous glow,
Red and yellow o'er the purple of the pines among the
  boulders
And the shaggy horror brooding on the sullen slopes
  below.
  Were they pines among the boulders
  Or the hair upon his shoulders?
We were only simple seamen, so of course we didn't know.
We were simple singing seamen, so of course we couldn't
  know.

But we crossed a plain of poppies, and we came upon a
  fountain
Not of water, but of jewels, like a spray of leaping fire;
And behind it, in an emerald glade, beneath a golden
  mountain
There stood a crystal palace, for a sailor to admire;
  For a troop of ghosts came round us,
  Which with leaves of bay they crowned us,
Then with grog they well-nigh drowned us, to the depth
  of our desire!
And 'twas very friendly of them, as a sailor can admire!

There was music all about us, we were growing quite
  forgetful
We were only singing seamen from the dirt of London-
  town,
Though the nectar that we swallowed seemed to vanish
  half regretful
As if we wasn't good enough to take such vittles down,
  When we saw a sudden figger,
  Tall and black as any nigger,

Like the devil—only bigger—drawing near us with a
    frown!
Like the devil—but much bigger—and he wore a golden
    crown!

And "What's all this?" he growls at us! With dignity we
    chaunted,
"Forty singing seamen, sir, as won't be put upon!"
"What? Englishmen?" he cries, "Well, if ye don't mind
    being haunted,
Faith, you're welcome to my palace; I'm the famous Prester
    John!
    Will ye walk into my palace?
    I don't bear 'ee any malice!
One and all ye shall be welcome in the halls of Prester
    John!"
So we walked into the palace and the halls of Prester John!

Now the door was one great diamond and the hall a
    hollow ruby—
Big as Beachy Head, my lads, nay, bigger by a half!
And I sees the mate wi' mouth agape, a-staring like a
    booby,
And the skipper close behind him, with his tongue out
    like a calf!
    Now the way to take it rightly
    Was to walk along politely
Just as if you didn't notice—so I couldn't help but laugh!
For they both forgot their manners and the crew was
    bound to laugh!

But he took us through his palace, and, my lads, as I'm a
    sinner,
We walked into an opal like a sunset-colored cloud—

"My dining room," he says, and, quick as light, we saw a dinner
Spread before us by the fingers of a hidden fairy crowd;
  And the skipper, swaying gently
  After dinner, murmurs faintly,
"I look to-wards you, Prester John, you've done us very proud!"
And he drank his health with honors, for he *done* us *very* proud!

Then he walks us to his gardens where we sees a feathered demon
Very splendid and important on a sort of spicy tree!
"That's the Phoenix," whispers Prester, "which all eddicated seamen
Knows the only one existent, and *he's* waiting for to flee!
  When his hundred years expire
  Then he'll set hisself afire
And another from his ashes rise most beautiful to see!
With wings of rose and emerald most beautiful to see!

Then he says, "In yonder forest there's a little silver river
And whosoever drinks of it, his youth will never die!
The centuries go by, but Prester John endures forever
With his music in the mountains and his magic on the sky!
  While *your* hearts are growing colder,
  While your world is growing older,
There's a magic in the distance, where the sea-line meets the sky.
It shall call to singing seamen till the fount o' song is dry!"

So we thought we'd up and seek it, but that forest fair defied us,—
First a crimson leopard laughed at us most horrible to see,

Then a sea-green lion came and sniffed and licked his
    chops and eyed us,
While a red and yellow unicorn was dancing round a tree!
  We was trying to look thinner,
  Which was hard, because our dinner
Must ha' made us very tempting to a cat o' high degree!
Must ha' made us very tempting to the whole menarjeree!

So we scuttled from that forest and across the poppy
    meadows
Where the awful shaggy horror brooded o'er us in the dark!
And we pushes out from shore again a-jumping at our
    shadows
And pulls away most joyful to the old black barque!
  And home again we plodded
  While Polyphemus nodded
With his battered moon-eye winking red and yellow
    through the dark.

Oh, the moon above the mountains red and yellow through
   the dark!

Across the seas of Wonderland to London-town we blun-
   dered,
Forty singing seamen as was puzzled for to know
If the visions that we saw was caused by—here again we
   pondered—
A tipple in a vision forty thousand years ago.
   Could the grog we *dreamt* we swallowed
   Make us *dream* of all that followed?
We were simply singing seamen, so of course we didn't
   know!
We were simply singing seamen, so of course we could not
   know!

Alfred Noyes

THE PRIEST AND THE
MULBERRY TREE

Did you hear of the curate who mounted his mare,
And merrily trotted along to the fair?
Of creature more tractable none ever heard;
In the height of her speed she would stop at a word;
But again with a word, when the curate said, "Hey,"
She put forth her mettle and gallop'd away.

As near to the gates of the city he rode,
While the sun of September all brilliantly glow'd,
The good priest discover'd, with eyes of desire,
A mulberry tree in a hedge of wild brier;
On boughs long and lofty, in many a green shoot,
Hung, large, black, and glossy, the beautiful fruit.

The curate was hungry and thirsty to boot;
He shrunk from the thorns, though he longed for the fruit;
With a word he arrested his courser's keen speed,
And he stood up erect on the back of his steed;
On the saddle he stood while the creature stood still,
And he gather'd the fruit till he took his good fill.

"Sure never," he thought, "was a creature so rare,
So docile, so true, as my excellent mare;
Lo, here now I stand," and he gazed all around,
"As safe and as steady as if on the ground;
Yet how had it been, if some traveller this way,
Had, dreaming no mischief, but chanced to cry, 'Hey'?"

He stood with his head in the mulberry tree,
And he spoke out aloud in his fond revery;
At the sound of the word the good mare made a push,
And down went the priest in the wild-brier bush.

He remember'd too late, on his thorny green bed,
Much that well may be thought cannot wisely be said.

Thomas Love Peacock

THE WAR-SONG OF
DINAS VAWR

The mountain sheep are sweeter,
But the valley sheep are fatter;
We therefore deemed it meeter
To carry off the latter.
We made an expedition;
We met a host, and quelled it;
We forced a strong position,
And killed the men who held it.

On Dyfed's richest valley,
Where herds of kine were browsing,
We made a mighty sally,
To furnish our carousing,
Fierce warriors rushed to meet us;
We met them, and o'erthrew them:
They struggled hard to beat us;
But we conquered them, and slew them.

As we drove our prize at leisure,
The king marched forth to catch us:
His rage surpassed all measure,
But his people could not match us.
He fled to his hall-pillars;
And, ere our force we led off,
Some sacked his house and cellars,
While others cut his head off.

We there, in strife bewild'ring,
Spilt blood enough to swim in:
We orphaned many children,
And widowed many women.
The eagles and the ravens
We glutted with our foemen;
The heroes and the cravens,
The spearmen and the bowmen.

We brought away from battle,
And much their land bemoaned them,
Two thousand head of cattle,
And the head of him who owned them:
Ednyfed, king of Dyfed,
His head was borne before us;
His wine and beasts supplied our feasts,
And his overthrow, our chorus.

Thomas Love Peacock

ANNABEL LEE

It was many and many a year ago,
   In a kingdom by the sea,
That a maiden there lived whom you may know
   By the name of Annabel Lee;—
And this maiden she lived with no other thought
   Than to love and be loved by me.

I was a child and *she* was a child,
   In this kingdom by the sea,
But we loved with a love that was more than love—
   I and my Annabel Lee—
With a love that the wingèd seraphs in Heaven
   Coveted her and me.

And this was the reason that, long ago,
    In this kingdom by the sea,
A wind blew out of a cloud, chilling
    My beautiful Annabel Lee;
So that her high-born kinsmen came
    And bore her away from me,
To shut her up in a sepulcher
    In this kingdom by the sea.

The angels, not half so happy in Heaven,
    Went envying her and me:—
Yes!—that was the reason (as all men know,
    In this kingdom by the sea)
That the wind came out of the cloud, by night,
    Chilling and killing my Annabel Lee.

But our love it was stronger by far than the love
    Of those who were older than we—
    Of many far wiser than we—
And neither the angels in Heaven above,
    Nor the demons down under the sea,
Can ever dissever my soul from the soul
    Of the beautiful Annabel Lee:—

For the moon never beams without bringing me dreams
    Of the beautiful Annabel Lee;
And the stars never rise but I feel the bright eyes
    Of the beautiful Annabel Lee;
And so, all the night-tide, I lie down by the side
Of my darling,—my darling,—my life and my bride,
    In her sepulcher there by the sea—
    In her tomb by the sounding sea.

Edgar Allan Poe

A LEGEND OF
LAKE OKEEFINOKEE

There once was a frog,
And he lived in a bog,
On the banks of Lake Okeefinokee.
And the words of the song
That he sang all day long
Were, "Croakety croakety croaky."

Said the frog, "I have found
That my life's daily round
In this place is exceedingly poky.
So no longer I'll stop,
But I swiftly will hop
Away from Lake Okeefinokee."

Now a bad mocking-bird
By mischance overheard
The words of the frog as he spokee.
And he said, "All my life
Frog and I've been at strife,
As we lived by Lake Okeefinokee.

"Now I see at a glance
Here's a capital chance
For to play him a practical jokee.
So I'll venture to say
That he shall not to-day
Leave the banks of Lake Okeefinokee."

So this bad mocking-bird,
Without saying a word,
He flew to a tree which was oaky;

And loudly he sang,
Till the whole forest rang,
"Oh! Croakety croakety croaky!"

As he warbled this song,
Master Frog came along,
A-filling his pipe for to smokee;
And he said, " 'Tis some frog
Has escaped from the bog
Of Okeefinokee-finokee.

"I am filled with amaze
To hear one of my race
A-warbling on top of an oaky;
But if frogs can climb trees,
I may still find some ease
On the banks of Lake Okeefinokee."

So he climbed up the tree;
But alas! down fell he!
And his lovely green neck it was brokee;
And the sad truth to say,
Never more did he stray
From the banks of Lake Okeefinokee.

And the bad mocking-bird
Said, "How very absurd
And delightful a practical jokee!"
But I'm happy to say
He was drowned the next day
In the waters of Okeefinokee.

Laura E. Richards

THE OLD MAN AND JIM

Old man never had much to say—
  'Ceptin' to Jim,
And Jim was the wildest boy he had—
  And the old man jes' wrapped up in him!
Never heerd him speak but once
Er twice in my life,—and first time was
When the army broke out, and Jim he went,
The old man backin' him, fer three months;
And all 'at I heerd the old man say
Was, jes' as we turned to start away,—
    "Well, good-by, Jim:
      Take keer of yourse'f!"

Peared-like, he was more satisfied
  Jes' *lookin'* at Jim
And likin' him all to hisse'f-like, see?—
  'Cause he was jes' wrapped up in him!
And over and over I mind the day
The old man come and stood round in the way
While we was drillin', a-watchin' Jim—
And down at the deepo a-heern' him say,
    "Well, good-by, Jim:
      Take keer of yourse'f!"

Never was nothin' about the *farm*
  Disting'ished Jim;
Neighbors all ust to wonder why
  The old man 'peared wrapped up in him:
But when Capt. Biggler he writ back
'At Jim was the bravest boy we had
In the whole dern rigiment, white er black,
And his fightin' good as his farmin' bad—

'At he had led, with a bullet clean
Bored through his thigh, and carried the flag
Through the bloodiest battle you ever seen,—
The old man wound up a letter to him
'At Cap. read to us, 'at said: "Tell Jim
   Good-by,
     And take keer of hisse'f."

Jim come home jes' long enough
   To take the whim
'At he'd like to go back in the cavelry—
   And the old man jes' wrapped up in him!
Jim 'lowed 'at he'd had sich luck afore,
Guessed he'd tackle her three years more.
And the old man give him a colt he'd raised,
And follered him over to Camp Ben Wade,
And laid eround fer a week er so,
Watchin' Jim on dress-parade;
'Tel finally he rid away,
And last he heered was the old man say,—
   "Well, good-by, Jim:
     Take keer of yourse'f!"

Tuk the papers, the old man did,
   A-watchin' fer Jim,
Fully believin' he'd make his mark
   Some way—jes' wrapped up in him!
And many a time the word 'ud come
'At stirred him up like the tap of a drum.
At Petersburg, fer instunce, where
Jim rid right into their cannons there,
And tuk 'em, and p'inted 'em t'other way
And socked it home to the boys in gray,
As they skooted fer timber, and on and on—
Jim a lieutenant,—and one arm gone,—

And the old man's words in his mind all day,—
  "Well, good-by, Jim:
    Take keer of yourse'f!"

Think of a private, now, perhaps,
  We'll say like Jim,
'At's clumb clean up to the shoulder-straps—
  And the old man jes' wrapped up in him!
Think of him—with the war plum' through,
And the glorious old Red-White-and-Blue
A-laughin' the news down over Jim,
And the old man, bendin' over him—
The surgeon turnin' away with tears
'At hadn't leaked fer years and years,
As the hand of the dyin' boy clung to
His father's, the old voice in his ears,—
  "Well, good-by, Jim:
    Take keer of yourse'f!"

James Whitcomb Riley

RICHARD CORY

When Richard Cory went down town,
We people on the pavement looked at him:
He was a gentleman from sole to crown,
Clean favored, and imperially slim.

And he was always quietly arrayed,
And he was always human when he talked;
But still he fluttered pulses when he said,
"Good-morning," and he glittered when he walked.

And he was rich—yes, richer than a king—
And admirably schooled in every grace:

In fine, we thought that he was everything
To make us wish that we were in his place.

So on we worked, and waited for the light,
And went without the meat, and cursed the bread;
And Richard Cory, one calm summer night,
Went home and put a bullet through his head.

Edwin Arlington Robinson

THE BLIND MEN AND
THE ELEPHANT

It was six men of Indostan,
   To learning much inclined,
Who went to see the Elephant
   (Though all of them were blind),
That each by observation
   Might satisfy his mind.

The First approached the Elephant,
   And happening to fall
Against his broad and sturdy side,
   At once began to bawl:
"God bless me! but the Elephant
   Is very like a wall!"

The Second, feeling of the tusk,
   Cried, "Ho! what have we here
So very round and smooth and sharp?
   To me 'tis mighty clear
This wonder of an Elephant
   Is very like a spear!"

The Third approached the animal,
   And happening to take
The squirming trunk within his hands,

Thus boldly up and spake:
"I see," quoth he, "the Elephant
Is very like a snake!"

The Fourth reached out his eager hand,
    And felt about the knee.
"What most this wondrous beast is like
    Is mighty plain," quoth he;
" 'Tis clear enough the Elephant
    Is very like a tree!"

The Fifth, who chanced to touch the ear,
    Said: "E'en the blindest man
Can tell what this resembles most;
    Deny the fact who can,
This marvel of an Elephant
    Is very like a fan!"

The Sixth no sooner had begun
    About the beast to grope,
Than, seizing on the swinging tail
    That fell within his scope,
"I see," quoth he, "the Elephant
    Is very like a rope!"

And so these men of Indostan
    Disputed loud and long,
Each in his own opinion
    Exceeding stiff and strong,
Though each was partly in the right,
    And all were in the wrong!

Moral

So oft in theologic wars,
    The disputants, I ween,

Rail on in utter ignorance
   Of what each other mean
And prate about an Elephant
   Not one of them has seen!

                John Godfrey Saxe

THE YOUTH AND
THE NORTHWIND

A Tale of Norway

Once on a time—'twas long ago—
   There lived a worthy dame
Who sent her son to fetch some flour,
   For she was old and lame.

But while he loitered on the road,
   The Northwind chanced to stray
Across the careless younker's path,
   And stole the flour away.

"Alas! what shall we do for bread?"
   Exclaimed the weeping lad;
"The flour is gone,—the flour is gone,—
   And it was all we had!"

And so he sought the Northwind's cave,
   Beside the distant main;
"Good Mister Boreas," said the lad,
   "I want my flour again.

" 'Twas all we had to live upon,—
   My mother old and I;
Oh give us back the flour again,
   Or we shall surely die!"

"I have it not," the Northwind growled;
　"But, for your lack of bread,'
I give to you this table-cloth;
　'Twill serve you well instead;

"For you have but to spread it out,
　And every costly dish
Will straight appear at your command,
　Whatever you may wish."

The lad received the magic cloth
　With wonder and delight,
And thanked the donor heartily,
　As well, indeed, he might.

Returning homeward, at an inn
　Just half his journey through,
He fain must show his table-cloth,
　And what the cloth could do.

So while he slept the knavish host
　Went slyly to his bed,
And stole the cloth,—but shrewdly placed
　Another in its stead.

Unknowing what the rogue had done,
　The lad went on his way,
And came unto his journey's end
　Just at the close of day.

He showed the dame his table-cloth,
　And told her of its power;
"Good sooth!" he cried, "'twas well for us
　The Northwind stole the flour."

"Perhaps," exclaimed the cautious crone,
    "The story may be true;
'Tis mighty little good, I ween,
    Your table-cloth can do."

And now the younker spread it forth,
    And tried the spell. Alas!
'Twas but a common table-cloth,
    And nothing came to pass.

Then to the Northwind, far away,
    He sped with might and main;
"Your table-cloth is good for naught;
    I want my flour again!"

"I have it not," the Northwind growled,
    "But, for your lack of bread,
I give to you this little goat,
    'Twill serve you well instead;

"For you have but to tell him this.
    'Make money, Master Bill!'
And he will give you golden coins,
    As many as you will."

The lad received the magic goat
    With wonder and delight,
And thanked the donor heartily,
    As well, indeed, he might.

Returning homeward, at the inn
    Just half his journey through,
He fain must show his little goat,
    And what the goat could do.

So while he slept the knavish host
  Went slyly to the shed,
And stole the goat,—but shrewdly placed
  Another in his stead.

Unknowing what the rogue had done,
  The youth went on his way,
And reached his weary journey's end
  Just at the close of day.

He showed the dame his magic goat,
  And told her of his power;
"Good sooth!" he cried, " 'twas well for us
  The Northwind stole the flour."

"I much misdoubt," the dame replied,
  "Your wondrous tale is true;
'Tis little good, for hungry folk,
  Your silly goat can do!"

"Good Master Bill," the lad exclaimed,
    "Make money!" but, alas!
'Twas nothing but a common goat,
    And nothing came to pass.

Then to the Northwind, angrily,
    He sped with might and main;
"Your foolish goat is good for naught;
    I want my flour again!"

"I have it not," the Northwind growled,
    "Nor can I give you aught,
Except this cudgel,—which, indeed,
    A magic charm has got;

"For you have but to tell it this:
    'My cudgel, hit away!'
And, till you bid it stop again,
    The cudgel will obey."

Returning home, he stopt at night
    Where he had lodged before;
And feigning to be fast asleep,
    He soon began to snore.

And when the host would steal the staff,
    The sleeper muttered, "Stay,
I see what you would fain be at;
    Good cudgel, hit away!"

The cudgel thumped about his ears,
    Till he began to cry,
"Oh stop the staff, for mercy's sake!
    Or I shall surely die!"

But still the cudgel thumped away
   Until the rascal said,
"I'll give you back the cloth and goat,
   Oh spare my broken head!"

And so it was the lad reclaimed
   His table-cloth and goat;
And, growing rich, at length became
   A man of famous note;

He kept his mother tenderly,
   And cheered her waning life;
And married—as you may suppose—
   A princess for a wife;

And while he lived had ever near,
   To favor worthy ends,
A cudgel for his enemies,
   And money for his friends.

                              John Godfrey Saxe

ALLEN-A-DALE

Allen-a-Dale has no fagot for burning,
Allen-a-Dale has no furrow for turning,
Allen-a-Dale has no fleece for the spinning,
Yet Allen-a-Dale has red gold for the winning.
Come, read me my riddle! come, hearken my tale!
And tell me the craft of bold Allen-a-Dale.

The Baron of Ravensworth prances in pride,
And he views his domains upon Arkindale side.
The mere for his net, and the land for his game,
The chase for the wild, and the park for the tame;

Yet the fish of the lake, and the deer of the vale
Are less free to Lord Dacre than Allen-a-Dale!

Allen-a-Dale was ne'er belted a knight,
Though his spur be as sharp, and his blade be as bright;
Allen-a-Dale is no baron or lord,
Yet twenty tall yeomen will draw at his word;
And the best of our nobles his bonnet will vail,
Who at Rere-cross on Stanmore meets Allen-a-Dale.

Allen-a-Dale to his wooing is come;
The mother, she asked of his household and home:
"Though the castle of Richmond stand fair on the hill,
My hall," quoth bold Allen, "shows gallanter still;
'Tis the blue vault of heaven, with its crescent so pale,
And with all its bright spangles!" said Allen-a-Dale.

The father was steel, and the mother was stone;
They lifted the latch, and they bade him be gone;
But loud, on the morrow, their wail and their cry:
He had laughed on the lass with his bonny black eye,
And she fled to the forest to hear a love-tale,
And the youth it was told by was Allen-a-Dale!

Sir Walter Scott

LOCHINVAR

O, young Lochinvar is come out of the west,
Through all the wide Border his steed was the best;
And save his good broadsword he weapons had none,
He rode all unarm'd and he rode all alone.
So faithful in love and so dauntless in war,
There never was knight like the young Lochinvar.

He staid not for brake, and he stopp'd not for stone,
He swam the Eske river where ford there was none;
But ere he alighted at Netherby gate,
The bride had consented; the gallant came late:
   For a laggard in love and a dastard in war,
   Was to wed the fair Ellen of brave Lochinvar.

So boldly he enter'd the Netherby Hall,
Among bride's-men and kinsmen and brothers and all:
Then spoke the bride's father, his hand on his sword,
(For the poor craven bridegroom said never a word):
   "O come ye in peace here, or come ye in war,
   Or to dance at our bridal, young Lord Lochinvar?"

"I long woo'd your daughter, my suit you denied;
Love swells like the Solway, but ebbs like its tide—
And now am I come, with this lost love of mine,
To lead but one measure, drink one cup of wine.
   There are maidens in Scotland more lovely by far,
   That would gladly be bride to the young Lochinvar."

The bride kiss'd the goblet: the knight took it up,
He quaff'd off the wine, and he threw down the cup.
She look'd down to blush and she look'd up to sigh,
With a smile on her lips, and a tear in her eye.
   He took her soft hand ere her mother could bar,
   "Now tread we a measure!" said young Lochinvar.

So stately his form, and so lovely her face,
That never a hall such a galliard did grace;
While her mother did fret, and her father did fume,
And the bridegroom stood dangling his bonnet and plume;
   And the bride-maidens whispered, " 'Twere better by far,
   To have matched our fair cousin with young Lochinvar."

One touch to her hand, and one word in her ear,
When they reach'd the hall-door, and the charger stood
      near;
So light to the croupe the fair lady he swung,
So light to the saddle before her he sprung!
  "She is won! We are gone, over bank, bush and scaur;
  They'll have fleet steeds that follow!" quoth young
    Lochinvar.

There was mounting 'mong Graemes of the Netherby clan;
Forsters, Fenwicks and Musgraves, they rode and they ran:
There was racing and chasing, on Cannobie Lee,
But the lost bride of Netherby ne'er did they see.
  So daring in love, and so dauntless in war,
  Have ye e'er heard of gallant like young Lochinvar?

                               Sir Walter Scott

THE CREMATION OF SAM McGEE

There are strange things done in the midnight sun
  By the men who moil for gold;
The Arctic trails have their secret tales
  That would make your blood run cold;
The Northern Lights have seen queer sights,
  But the queerest they ever did see
Was that night on the marge of Lake Lebarge
  I cremated Sam McGee.

Now Sam McGee was from Tennessee, where the cotton
    blooms and blows.
Why he left his home in the South to roam 'round the Pole,
    God only knows.

He was always cold, but the land of gold seemed to hold
    him like a spell;
Though he'd often say in his homely way that "he'd sooner
    live in hell."

On a Christmas day we were mushing our way over the
    Dawson trail.
Talk of your cold! through the parka's fold it stabbed like
    a driven nail.
If our eyes we'd close, then the lashes froze till sometimes
    we couldn't see;
It wasn't much fun, but the only one to whimper was Sam
    McGee.

And that very night, as we lay packed tight in our robes
    beneath the snow,
And the dogs were fed, and the stars o'erhead were danc-
    ing heel and toe,
He turned to me, and "Cap," says he, "I'll cash in this trip,
    I guess;
And if I do, I'm asking that you won't refuse my last
    request."

Well, he seemed so low that I couldn't say no; then he says
    with a sort of moan:
"It's the cursèd cold, and it's got right hold till I'm chilled
    clean through to the bone.
Yet 'tain't being dead—it's my awful dread of the icy grave
    that pains;
So I want you to swear that, foul or fair, you'll cremate my
    last remains."

A pal's last need is a thing to heed, so I swore I would not
    fail;
And we started on at the streak of dawn; but God! he
    looked ghastly pale.

He crouched on the sleigh, and he raved all day of his
    home in Tennessee;
And before nightfall a corpse was all that was left of Sam
    McGee.

There wasn't a breath in that land of death, and I hurried,
    horror-driven,
With a corpse half hid that I couldn't get rid, because of a
    promise given;
It was lashed to the sleigh, and it seemed to say: "You may
    tax your brawn and brains,
But you promised true, and it's up to you to cremate these
    last remains."

Now a promise made is a debt unpaid, and the trail has its
    own stern code.
In the days to come, though my lips were dumb, in my
    heart how I cursed that load.
In the long, long night, by the lone firelight, while the
    huskies, round in a ring,
Howled out their woes to the homeless snows—O God!
    how I loathed the thing.

And every day that quiet clay seemed to heavy and
    heavier grow;
And on I went, though the dogs were spent and the grub
    was getting low;
The trail was bad, and I felt half mad, but I swore I
    would not give in;
And I'd often sing to the hateful thing, and it hearkened
    with a grin.

Till I came to the marge of Lake Lebarge, and a derelict
    there lay;
It was jammed in the ice, but I saw in a trice it was called
    the "Alice May."

And I looked at it, and I thought a bit, and I looked at
    my frozen chum;
Then "Here," said I, with a sudden cry, "is my cre-ma-
    tor-eum."

Some planks I tore from the cabin floor, and I lit the boiler
    fire;
Some coal I found that was lying around, and I heaped
    the fuel higher;
The flames just soared, and the furnace roared—such a
    blaze you seldom see;
And I burrowed a hole in the glowing coal, and I stuffed
    in Sam McGee.

Then I made a hike, for I didn't like to hear him sizzle so;
And the heavens scowled, and the huskies howled, and the
    wind began to blow.
It was icy cold, but the hot sweat rolled down my cheeks,
    and I don't know why;
And the greasy smoke in an inky cloak went streaking
    down the sky.

I do not know how long in the snow I wrestled with grisly
    fear;
But the stars came out and they danced about ere again I
    ventured near;

I was sick with dread, but I bravely said: "I'll just take a
     peep inside.
I guess he's cooked, and it's time I looked"; . . . then the
     door I opened wide.

And there sat Sam, looking cool and calm, in the heart of
     the furnace roar;
And he wore a smile you could see a mile, and he said:
     "Please close that door.
It's fine in here, but I greatly fear you'll let in the cold and
     storm—
Since I left Plumtree down in Tennessee, it's the first time
     I've been warm."

There are strange things done in the midnight sun
   By the men who moil for gold;
The Arctic trails have their secret tales
   That would make your blood run cold;
The Northern Lights have seen queer sights,
   But the queerest they ever did see
Was that night on the marge of Lake Lebarge
   I cremated Sam McGee.

                                Robert W. Service

BALLAD OF
THE LITTLE BLACK HOUND

Who knocks at the Geraldine's* door to-night
   In the black storm and the rain?
With the thunder crash and the shrieking wind
   Comes the moan of a creature's pain.

* An Irish earl.

And once they knocked, yet never a stir
   To show that the Geraldine knew;
And twice they knocked, yet never a bolt
   The listening Geraldine drew.

And thrice they knocked ere he moved his chair,
   And said, "Whoever it be,
I dare not open the door to-night
   For a fear has come to me."

Three times he rises from out his chair,
   And three times he sits him down.
"Now what has made faint this heart of mine?"
   He says with a growing frown.

"Now what has made me a coward to-night.
   Who never knew fear before?
But I swear that the hand of a little child
   Keeps pulling me from the door."

The Geraldine rose from his chair at last
   And opened the door full wide;
"Whoever is out in the storm," said he,
   "May in God's name come inside!"

He who was out in the storm and rain
   Drew back at the Geraldine's call.
"Now who comes not in the Holy Name
   Will never come in at all."

He looked to the right, he looked to the left,
   And never a one saw he;
But right in his path lay a coal black hound,
   A-moaning right piteously.

"Come in," he cried, "you little black hound,
    Come in, I will ease your pain;
My roof shall keep you to-night at least
    From the lash of wind and rain."

The Geraldine took up the little black hound,
    And put him down by the fire.
"So sleep you there, poor wandering one,
    As long as your heart desire."

The Geraldine tossed on his bed that night,
    And never asleep went he
For the crowing of his little red cock,
    That did crow most woefully.

For the howling of his own wolf-hound,
    That cried at the gate all night.
He rose and went to the banquet hall
    At the first of morning light.

He looked to the right, he looked to the left,
    At the rug where the dog lay on;
But the reindeer skin was burnt in two,
    And the little black hound was gone.

And, traced in the ashes, these words he read:
    "For the soul of your first-born son,
I will make you rich as you once were rich
    Ere the glass of your luck was run."

The Geraldine went to the west window,
    And then he went to the east,
And saw his desolate pasture fields,
    And the stables without a beast.

"So be it, as I love no woman,
  No son shall ever be mine;
I would that my stables were full of steeds,
  And my cellars were full of wine."

"I swear it, as I love no woman,
  And never a son have I,
I would that my sheep and their little lambs
  Should flourish and multiply.

So yours be the soul of my first-born son."
  Here the Geraldine slyly smiled,
But from the dark of the lonely room
  Came the cry of a little child.

The Geraldine went to the west window,
  He opened and out did lean,
And lo! the pastures were full of kine,
  All chewing the grass so green.

And quickly he went to the east window,
  And his face was pale to see,
For lo! he saw to the empty stalls
  Brave steeds go three by three.

The Geraldine went to the great hall door,
  In wonder at what had been,
And there he saw the prettiest maid,
  That ever his eyes had seen.

And long he looked at the pretty young maid,
  And swore there was none so fair;
And his heart went out of him like a hound,
  And hers like a timid hare.

Each day he followed her up and down,
 And each night he could not rest,
Until at last the pretty young maid
 Her love for him confessed.

They wooed and they wed, and the days went by
 As quick as such good days will,
And at last came the cry of his first-born son
 The cup of his joy to fill.

And the summer passed, and the winter came;
 Right fair was the child to see,
And he laughed at the shriek of a bitter storm
 As he sat on his father's knee.

Who rings so loud at the Geraldine's gate?
 Who knocks so loud at the door?
"Now rise you up, my pretty young wife,
 For twice they have knocked before."

Quickly she opened the great hall door,
 And "Welcome you in," she cried,
But there only entered a little black hound,
 And he would not be denied.

When the Geraldine saw the little black dog,
 He rose with a fearful cry,
"I sold my child to the Devil's hound
 In forgotten days gone by."

He drew his sword on the little black hound,
 But it would not pierce its skin,
He tried to pray, but his lips were dumb
 Because of his grievous sin.

Then the fair young wife took the black hound's throat
   Both her small white hands between.
And he thought he saw one of God's angels
   Where his sweet young wife had been.

Then he thought he saw from God's spirit
   The hound go sore oppressed,
But he woke to find his own dead wife
   With her dead child on her breast.

Quickly he went to the west window,
   Quickly he went to the east;
No help in the desolate pasture fields,
   Or the stables that held no beast.

He flung himself at his white wife's side,
   And the dead lips moved and smiled,
Then came somewhere from the lonely room
   The laugh of a little child.

Dora Sigerson Shorter

BISHOP HATTO

The summer and autumn had been so wet
That in winter the corn was growing yet;
'Twas a piteous sight to see all around
The grain lie rotting on the ground.

Every day the starving poor
Crowded around Bishop Hatto's door,
For he had a plentiful last year's store,
And all the neighbourhood could tell
His granaries were furnish'd well.

At last Bishop Hatto appointed a day
To quiet the poor without delay;
He bade them to his great barn repair,
And they should have food for the winter there.

Rejoiced such tidings good to hear,
The poor folk flock'd from far and near;
The great barn was full as it could hold
Of women and children, and young and old.

Then when he saw it could hold no more,
Bishop Hatto he made fast the door;
And while for mercy on Christ they call,
He set fire to the barn and burnt them all.

"I' faith, 'tis an excellent bonfire!" quoth he,
"And the country is greatly obliged to me,
For ridding it in these times forlorn
Of rats, that only consume the corn."

So then to his palace returned he,
And he sat down to supper merrily,
And he slept that night like an innocent man
But Bishop Hatto never slept again.

In the morning as he enter'd the hall,
Where his picture hung against the wall,
A sweat like death all over him came,
For the rats had eaten it out of the frame.

As he look'd there came a man from the farm,
He had a countenance white with alarm;
"My lord, I open'd your granaries this morn,
And the rats had eaten all your corn."

Another came running presently,
And he was pale as pale could be,
"Fly! my Lord Bishop, fly," quoth he,
"Ten thousand rats are coming this way—
The Lord forgive you for yesterday!"

"I'll go to my tower on the Rhine," replied he,
" 'Tis the safest place in Germany;
The walls are high, and the shores are steep,
And the stream is strong, and the water deep."

Bishop Hatto fearfully hasten'd away,
And he cross'd the Rhine without delay,
And reach'd his tower, and barr'd with care
All the windows, doors, and loopholes there.

He laid him down and closed his eyes,
But soon a scream made him arise;
He started, and saw two eyes of flame
On his pillow from whence the screaming came.

He listen'd and look'd; it was only the cat;
But the Bishop he grew more fearful for that,
For she sat screaming, mad with fear,
At the army of rats that was drawing near.

For they have swum over the river so deep,
And they have climb'd the shores so steep,
And up the tower their way is bent
To do the work for which they were sent.

They are not to be told by the dozen or score,
By thousands they come, and by myriads and more;
Such numbers had never been heard of before,
Such a judgment had never been witness'd of yore.

Down on his knees the Bishop fell,
And faster and faster his beads did he tell,
As louder and louder drawing near
The gnawing of their teeth he could hear.

And in at the windows, and in at the door,
And through the walls helter-skelter they pour,
And down from the ceiling, and up through the floor,
From the right and the left, from behind and before,
From within and without, from above and below,
And all at once to the Bishop they go.

They have whetted their teeth against the stones,
And now they pick the Bishop's bones;
They gnaw'd the flesh from every limb,
For they were sent to do judgment on him.

Robert Southey

CHRISTMAS AT SEA

The sheets were frozen hard, and they cut the naked hand;
The decks were like a slide, where a seaman scarce could
    stand;
The wind was a nor'wester, blowing squally off the sea;
And cliffs and spouting breakers were the only things a-lee.

They heard the surf a-roaring before the break of day;
But 'twas only with the peep of light we saw how ill we lay.
We tumbled every hand on deck instanter, with a shout,
And we gave her the maintops'l, and stood by to go about.

All day we tacked and tacked between the South Head
    and the North;
All day we hauled the frozen sheets, and got no further
    forth;
All day as cold as charity, in bitter pain and dread,
For very life and nature we tacked from head to head.

We gave the South a wider berth, for there the tide race
    roared;
But every tack we made we brought the North Head close
    aboard:
So's we saw the cliffs and houses, and the breakers run-
    ning high,
And the coastguard in his garden, with his glass against
    his eye.

The frost was on the village roofs as white as ocean foam;
The good red fires were burning bright in every 'long-shore
    home;
The windows sparkled clear, and the chimneys volleyed
    out;
And I vow we sniffed the victuals as the vessel went about.

The bells upon the church were rung with a mighty jovial
    cheer;
For it's just that I should tell you how (of all days in the
    year)
This day of our adversity was blessèd Christmas morn,
And the house above the coastguard's was the house where
    I was born.

O well I saw the pleasant room, the pleasant faces there,
My mother's silver spectacles, my father's silver hair;
And well I saw the firelight, like a flight of homely elves,
Go dancing round the china-plates that stand upon the
    shelves.

And well I knew the talk they had, the talk that was of me,
Of the shadow on the household and the son that went to
    sea;
And O the wicked fool I seemed, in every kind of way,
To be here and hauling frozen ropes on blessèd Christmas
    Day.

They lit the high sea-light, and the dark began to fall.
"All hands to loose topgallant sails," I heard the captain
    call.
"By the Lord, she'll never stand it," our first mate, Jackson,
    cried.
. . . "It's the one way or the other, Mr. Jackson," he replied.

She staggered to her bearings, but the sails were new and
    good,
And the ship smelt up to windward just as though she
    understood.
As the winter's day was ending, in the entry of the night,
We cleared the weary headland, and passed below the
    light.

And they heaved a mighty breath, every soul on board
      but me,
As they saw her nose again pointing handsome out to sea;
But all that I could think of, in the darkness and the cold,
Was just that I was leaving home and my folks were grow-
      ing old.

Robert Louis Stevenson

BAUCIS AND PHILEMON

In ancient times, as story tells,
The saints would often leave their cells,
And stroll about, but hide their quality,
To try good people's hospitality.
It happened on a winter night,
As authors of the legend write,
Two brother hermits, saints by trade.
Taking their tour in masquerade,
Disguised in tattered garments went
To a small village down in Kent;
Where in the stroller's canting strain,
They begged from door to door in vain;
Tried every tone might pity win,
But not a soul would take them in.

Our wandering saints, in woful state,
Treated at this ungodly rate,
Having through all the village passed,
To a small cottage came at last
Where dwelt a good old honest yeoman,
Call'd in the neighborhood Philemon;
Who kindly did these saints invite
In his poor hut to pass the night;

And then the hospitable sire
Bid goody Baucis mend the fire;
While he from out the chimney took
A flitch of bacon off the hook,
And freely from the fattest side
Cut out large slices to be fried;
Then stepped aside to fetch them drink,
Filled a large jug up to the brink,
And saw it fairly twice go round;
Yet (what is wonderful) they found
'Twas still replenished to the top,
As if they ne'er had touched a drop.
The good old couple were amazed,
And often on each other gazed;
For both were frightened to the heart,
And just began to cry, "What art!"
Then softly turned aside to view
Whether the lights were burning blue.

"Good folks, ye need not be afraid;
We are but saints," the hermits said;
"No hurt shall come to you or yours;
But for that pack of churlish boors,
Not fit to live on Christian ground,
They and their houses shall be drowned;
Whilst you shall see your cottage rise,
And grow a church before your eyes."

They scarce had spoke, when fair and soft,
The roof began to mount aloft,
Aloft rose every beam and rafter,
The heavy wall climbed slowly after;
The chimney widened and grew higher,
Became a steeple with a spire.
The kettle to the top was hoist,
And there stood fastened to a joist;
Doomed ever in suspense to dwell,
'Tis now no kettle, but a bell.
A wooden jack which had almost
Lost by disuse the art to roast,
A sudden alteration feels,
Increased by new intestine wheels;
The jack and chimney, near allied,
Had never left each other's side:
The chimney to a steeple grown,
The jack would not be left alone;
But up against the steeple reared,
Became a clock, and still adhered.
The groaning chair began to crawl,
Like a huge snail, along the wall;
There stuck aloft in public view,
And with small change a pulpit grew.
The cottage, by such feats as these,
Grown to a church by just degrees,
The hermits then desired the host
To ask for what he fancied most.
Philemon, having paused awhile,
Returned them thanks in homely style:
"I'm old, and fain would live at ease;
Make me the parson, if you please."

Thus happy in their change of life
Were several years this man and wife.

When on a day which proved their last,
Discoursing on old stories past,
They went by chance, amidst their talk,
To the churchyard to take a walk;
When Baucis hastily cried out,
"My dear, I see your forehead sprout!"
"But yes! Methinks I feel it true;
And really yours is budding too.
Nay,—now I cannot stir my foot;
It feels as if 'twere taking root!"
Description would but tire my muse;
In short, they both were turned to yews.

Jonathan Swift

THE THREE SONGS

King Siegfried sat in his lofty hall:
"Ye Harpers! who sings the best song of all?"
Then a youth stepped forth with a scornful lip,
The harp in his hand, and the sword at his hip.

"Three songs I know; but this first song
Thou, O King! has forgotten long:
Thou hast stabbed my brother with murderous hand,—
Hast stabbed my brother with murderous hand!

"The second song I learned aright
In the midst of a dark and stormy night;
Thou must fight with me for life or death,—
Must fight with me for life or death!"

On the banquet-table he laid his harp,
And they both drew out their swords so sharp;

And they fought in the sight of the harpers all,
Till the King sank dead in the lofty hall.

"And now for the third, the proudest, best!
I shall sing it, sing it, and never rest:
King Siegfried lies in his red, red blood,—
Siegfried lies in his red, red blood!"

Bayard Taylor

LADY CLARE

It was the time when lilies blow
   And clouds are highest up in air;
Lord Ronald brought a lily-white doe
   To give his cousin, Lady Clare.

I trow they did not part in scorn:
   Lovers long-betroth'd were they:
They too will wed the morrow morn:
   God's blessing on the day!

"He does not love me for my birth,
   Nor for my lands so broad and fair;
He loves me for my own true worth,
   And that is well," said Lady Clare.

In there came old Alice the nurse;
   Said: "Who was this that went from thee?"
"It was my cousin," said Lady Clare;
   "To-morrow he weds with me."

"O God be thank'd!" said Alice the nurse,
   "That all comes round so just and fair:
Lord Ronald is heir of all your lands,
   And you are not the Lady Clare."

"Are ye out of your mind, my nurse, my nurse,"
  Said Lady Clare, "that ye speak so wild?"
"As God's above," said Alice the nurse,
  "I speak the truth: you are my child.

"The old Earl's daughter died at my breast;
  I speak the truth, as I live by bread!
I buried her like my own sweet child,
  And put my child in her stead."

"Falsely, falsely have ye done,
  O mother," she said, "if this be true,
To keep the best man under the sun
  So many years from his due."

"Nay now, my child," said Alice the nurse,
  "But keep the secret for your life,
And all you have will be Lord Ronald's
  When you are man and wife."

"If I'm a beggar born," she said,
  "I will speak out, for I dare not lie.
Pull off, pull off the brooch of gold,
  And fling the diamond necklace by."

"Nay now, my child," said Alice the nurse,
  "But keep the secret all ye can."
She said: "Not so: but I will know
  If there be any faith in man."

"Nay now, what faith?" said Alice the nurse,
  "The man will cleave unto his right."
"And he shall have it," the lady replied,
  "Though I should die to-night."

"Yet give one kiss to your mother dear!
  Alas, my child, I sinn'd for thee."
"O mother, mother, mother," she said,
  "So strange it seems to me.

"Yet here's a kiss for my mother dear,
  My mother dear, if this be so,
And lay your hand upon my head,
  And bless me, mother, ere I go."

She clad herself in a russet gown,
  She was no longer Lady Clare:
She went by dale, she went by down,
  With a single rose in her hair.

The lily-white doe Lord Ronald had brought
  Leapt up from where she lay,
Dropt her head in the maiden's hand,
  And follow'd her all the way.

Down stept Lord Ronald from his tower:
  "O Lady Clare, you shame your worth!
Why come you drest like a village maid,
  That are the flower of the earth?"

"If I come drest like a village maid,
  I am but as my fortunes are:
I am a beggar born," she said,
  "And not the Lady Clare."

"Play me no tricks," said Lord Ronald,
  "For I am yours in word and deed.
Play me no tricks," said Lord Ronald,
  "Your riddle is hard to read."

O and proudly stood she up!
    Her heart within her did not fail:
She look'd into Lord Ronald's eyes,
    And told him all her nurse's tale.

He laugh'd a laugh of merry scorn:
    He turn'd and kissed her where she stood:
"If you are not the heiress born,
    And I," said he, "the next in blood—

"If you are not the heiress born,
    And I," said he, "the lawful heir,
We two will wed to-morrow morn,
    And you shall still be Lady Clare."

Alfred, Lord Tennyson

CASEY AT THE BAT

It looked extremely rocky for the Mudville nine that day;
The score stood two to four, with but one inning left to
    play.
So, when Cooney died at second, and Burrows did the
    same,
A pallor wreathed the features of the patrons of the game.

A straggling few got up to go, leaving there the rest,
With that hope which springs eternal within the human
    breast.
For they thought: "If only Casey could get a whack at
    that,"
They'd put even money now, with Casey at the bat.

But Flynn preceded Casey, and likewise so did Blake,
And the former was a pudd'n, and the latter was a fake.

So on that stricken multitude a deathlike silence sat;
For there seemed but little chance of Casey's getting to
the bat.

But Flynn let drive a single, to the wonderment of all.
And the much-despised Blakey "tore the cover off the
ball."
And when the dust had lifted, and they saw what had
occurred,
There was Blakey safe at second, and Flynn a-huggin'
third.

Then from the gladdened multitude went up a joyous
yell—
It rumbled in the mountaintops, it rattled in the dell;
It struck upon the hillside and rebounded on the flat;
For Casey, mighty Casey, was advancing to the bat.

There was ease in Casey's manner as he stepped into his
place,
There was pride in Casey's bearing and a smile on Casey's
face;
And when responding to the cheers he lightly doffed his
hat,
No stranger in the crowd could doubt 'twas Casey at the
bat.

Ten thousand eyes were on him as he rubbed his hands
with dirt,
Five thousand tongues applauded when he wiped them on
his shirt;
Then when the writhing pitcher ground the ball into his
hip,
Defiance gleamed from Casey's eye, a sneer curled Casey's
lip.

And now the leather-covered sphere came hurtling through
    the air,
And Casey stood a-watching it in haughty grandeur there.
Close by the sturdy batsman the ball unheeded sped;
"That ain't my style," said Casey. "Strike one," the umpire
    said.

From the benches, black with people, there went up a
    muffled roar,
Like the beating of the storm waves on the stern and dis-
    tant shore.
"Kill him! kill the umpire!" shouted someone on the stand;
And it's likely they'd have killed him had not Casey raised
    his hand.

With a smile of Christian charity great Casey's visage
    shone;
He stilled the rising tumult, he made the game go on;
He signaled to the pitcher, and once more the spheroid
    flew;
But Casey still ignored it, and the umpire said, "Strike
    two."

"Fraud!" cried the maddened thousands, and the echo an-
    swered "Fraud!"
But one scornful look from Casey and the audience was
    awed;
They saw his face grow stern and cold, they saw his mus-
    cles strain,
And they knew that Casey wouldn't let the ball go by
    again.

The sneer is gone from Casey's lips, his teeth are clenched
    in hate,
He pounds with cruel vengeance his bat upon the plate;

And now the pitcher holds the ball, and now he lets it go,
And now the air is shattered by the force of Casey's blow.

Oh, somewhere in this favored land the sun is shining
    bright,
The band is playing somewhere, and somewhere hearts
    are light;
And somewhere men are laughing, and somewhere chil-
    dren shout,
But there is no joy in Mudville—mighty Casey has struck
    out.

Ernest Lawrence Thayer

IN HARDIN COUNTY, 1809

With flintlocked guns and polished stocks,
Knee breeches and long homespun socks,
On morning of St. Valentine
Two hunters met in 1809.
Across the line from Illinois;
They stopped their mules and voiced their joy.

"Why, Ben, it's been a quite a spell
Since I've seen you. The folks all well?
Bring any news from up near town?"
"Why, yes. D'you know John Ezry Brown?
They say that he's a-goin down
To Washington in all the din
To see Jim Madison sworn in.

"And this young feller Bonaparte
That's fightin' cross the sea,
Is slicin' Europe all to bits.

Least that's what they're a tellin' me."
"Wal, wal, nice day, kinda breezy,
This mule's gettin' quite uneasy.

"Now come and see us some time, do,
And bring the gals and Hepsy, too."
"Yes, some fine day we'll be along,
Got any news to send along?"
"No, nothin' worth a tinker's song.
There's nothin' happens here near me,
Doggondest place you ever see.

"Tom Lincoln lives right over there,
In that log cabin, bleak and bare,
They say they have a little babe,
I understand they've named him 'Abe.'
Yes, Sally said just 'tother day,
That nothin' happens down this way."

Lulu E. Thompson

MOLLY MEANS

Old Molly Means was a hag and a witch;
Chile of the devil, the dark, and sitch.
Her heavy hair hung thick in ropes
And her blazing eyes was black as pitch.
Imp at three and wench at 'leben
She counted her husbands to the number seben.
    O Molly, Molly, Molly Means
    There goes the ghost of Molly Means.

Some say she was born with a veil on her face
So she could look through unnatchal space
Through the future and through the past
And charm a body or an evil place
And every man could well despise
The evil look in her coal black eyes.
    Old Molly, Molly, Molly Means
    Dark is the ghost of Molly Means.

And when the tale begun to spread
Of evil and of holy dread:
Her black-hand arts and her evil powers
How she cast her spells and called the dead,
The younguns was afraid at night
And the farmers feared their crops would blight.
    Old Molly, Molly, Molly Means
    Cold is the ghost of Molly Means.

Then one dark day she put a spell
On a young gal-bride just come to dwell
In the lane just down from Molly's shack
And when her husband come riding back

His wife was barking like a dog
And on all fours like a common hog.
    O Molly, Molly, Molly Means
    Where is the ghost of Molly Means?

The neighbors come and they went away
And said she'd die before break of day
But her husband held her in his arms
And swore he'd break the wicked charms;
He'd search all up and down the land
And turn the spell on Molly's hand.
    O Molly, Molly, Molly Means
    Sharp is the ghost of Molly Means.

So he rode all day and he rode all night
And at the dawn he come in sight
Of a man who said he could move the spell
And cause the awful thing to dwell
On Molly Means, to bark and bleed
Till she died at the hands of her evil deed.
    Old Molly, Molly, Molly Means
    This is the ghost of Molly Means.

Sometimes at night through the shadowy trees
She rides along on a winter breeze.
You can hear her holler and whine and cry.
Her voice is thin and her moan is high,
And her cackling laugh or her barking cold
Bring terror to the young and old.
    O Molly, Molly, Molly Means
    Lean is the ghost of Molly Means.

Margaret Walker

THE SPINNING WHEEL

Mellow the moonlight to shine is beginning,
Close by the window young Eileen is spinning;
Bent over the fire her blind grandmother, sitting,
Is crooning, and moaning, and drowsily knitting:—
"Eileen, achora, I hear someone tapping."
" 'Tis the ivy, dear mother, against the glass flapping."
"Eily, I surely hear somebody sighing."
" 'Tis the sound, mother dear, of the summer wind dying."
Merrily, cheerily, noiselessly whirring,
Swings the wheel, spins the wheel, while the foot's stirring;
Sprightly, and brightly, and airily ringing
Thrills the sweet voice of the young maiden singing.

"What's that noise that I hear at the window, I wonder?"
" 'Tis the little birds chirping the holly-bush under."
"What makes you be shoving and moving your stool on,
And singing, all wrong, that old song of 'The Coolun'?"
There's a form at the casement—the form of her true love—
And he whispers, with face bent, "I'm waiting for you,
            love;
Get up on the stool, through the lattice step lightly,
We'll rove in the grove, while the moon's shining brightly."
Merrily, cheerily, noiselessly whirring,
Swings the wheel, spins the wheel, while the foot's stirring;
Sprightly, and brightly, and airily ringing
Thrills the sweet voice of the young maiden singing.

The maid shakes her head, on her lips lays her fingers,
Steals up from her seat—longs to go, and yet lingers;
A frightened glance turns to her drowsy grandmother,
Puts one foot on the stool, spins the wheel with the other,
Lazily, easily, swings now the wheel round,
Slowly and lowly is heard now the reel's sound;

Noiseless and light to the lattice above her
The maid steps—then leaps to the arms of her lover.
Slower—and slower—and slower the wheel swings;
Lower—and lower—and lower the reel rings;
Ere the reel and the wheel stopped their ringing and
     moving,
Through the grove the young lovers by moonlight are
     roving.

                              John Francis Waller

SKIPPER IRESON'S RIDE

Of all the rides since the birth of time,
Told in story or sung in rhyme,—
On Apuleius's Golden Ass,
Or one-eyed Calender's horse of brass,
Witch astride of a human back,
Islam's prophet on Al-Borák,—
The strangest ride that ever was sped
Was Ireson's, out from Marblehead!
   Old Floyd Ireson, for his hard heart,
     Tarred and feathered and carried in a cart
       By the women of Marblehead!

Body of turkey, head of owl,
Wings a-droop like a rained-on fowl,
Feathered and ruffled in every part,
Skipper Ireson stood in the cart.
Scores of women, old and young,
Strong of muscle, and glib of tongue,
Pushed and pulled up the rocky lane,
Shouting and singing the shrill refrain:
   "Here's Flud Oirson, fur his horrd horrt,
     Torr'd an' futherr'd an' corr'd in a corrt
       By the women o' Morble'ead!"

Wrinkled scolds with hands on hips,
Girls in bloom of cheek and lips,
Wild-eyed, free-limbed, such as chase
Bacchus round some antique vase,
Brief of skirt, with ankles bare,
Loose of kerchief and loose of hair,
With conch-shells blowing and fish-horns' twang,
Over and over the Maenads sang:
    "Here's Flud Oirson, fur his horrd horrt,
    Torr'd an' futherr'd an' corr'd in a corrt
        By the women o' Morble'ead!"

Small pity for him!—He sailed away
From a leaking ship in Chaleur Bay,—
Sailed away from a sinking wreck,
With his own town's-people on her deck!
"Lay by! lay by!" they called to him.
Back he answered, "Sink or swim!
Brag of your catch of fish again!"
And off he sailed through the fog and rain!
  Old Floyd Ireson, for his hard heart,
    Tarred and feathered and carried in a cart
    By the women of Marblehead!

Fathoms deep in dark Chaleur
That wreck shall lie forevermore.
Mother and sister, wife and maid,
Looked from the rocks of Marblehead
Over the moaning and rainy sea,—
Looked for the coming that might not be!
What did the winds and the sea-birds say
Of the cruel captain who sailed away?—
   Old Floyd Ireson, for his hard heart,
    Tarred and feathered and carried in a cart
     By the women of Marblehead!

Through the street, on either side,
Up flew windows, doors swung wide;
Sharp-tongued spinsters, old wives gray,
Treble lent the fish-horn's bray.
Sea-worn grandsires, cripple-bound,
Hulks of old sailors run aground,
Shook head, and fist, and hat, and cane,
And cracked with curses the hoarse refrain:
   "Here's Flud Oirson, fur his horrd horrt,
    Torr'd an' futherr'd an' corr'd in a corrt
     By the women o' Morble'ead!"

Sweetly along the Salem road
Bloom of orchard and lilac showed.
Little the wicked skipper knew
Of the fields so green and the sky so blue.
Riding there in his sorry trim,
Like an Indian idol glum and grim,
Scarcely he seemed the sound to hear
Of voices shouting, far and near:
   "Here's Flud Oirson, fur his horrd horrt,
    Torr'd an' futherr'd an' corr'd in a corrt
     By the women o' Morble'ead!"

"Hear me, neighbors!" at last he cried,—
"What to me is this noisy ride?
What is the shame that clothes the skin
To the nameless horror that lives within?
Waking or sleeping, I see a wreck,
And hear a cry from a reeling deck!
Hate me and curse me,—I only dread
The hand of God and the face of the dead!"
  Said old Floyd Ireson, for his hard heart,
  Tarred and feathered and carried in a cart
    By the women of Marblehead!

Then the wife of the skipper lost at sea
Said, "God has touched him! why should we!"
Said an old wife mourning her only son,
"Cut the rogue's tether and let him run!"
So with soft relentings and rude excuse,
Half scorn, half pity, they cut him loose,
And gave him a cloak to hide him in,
And left him alone with his shame and sin.
  Poor Floyd Ireson, for his hard heart,
  Tarred and feathered and carried in a cart
    By the women of Marblehead!

                    John Greenleaf Whittier

KENTUCKY BELLE

Summer of 'sixty-three, sir, and Conrad was gone away—
Gone to the county town, sir, to sell our first load of hay.
We lived in the log house yonder, poor as ever you've seen;
Roschen there was a baby, and I was only nineteen.

Conrad, he took the oxen, but he left Kentucky Belle;
How much we thought of Kentuck, I couldn't begin to
    tell—

Came from the Bluegrass country; my father gave her to me
When I rode north with Conrad, away from the
Tennessee.

Conrad lived in Ohio—a German he is, you know—
The house stood in broad cornfields, stretching on, row
after row;
The old folks made me welcome; they were kind as kind
could be;
But I kept longing, longing, for the hills of the Tennessee.

O, for a sight of water, the shadowed slope of a hill!
Clouds that hang on the summit, a wind that never is still!
But the level land went stretching away to meet the sky—
Never a rise from north to south, to rest the weary eye!

From east to west, no river to shine out under the moon,
Nothing to make a shadow in the yellow afternoon;
Only the breathless sunshine, as I looked out, all forlorn,
Only the "rustle, rustle," as I walked among the corn.

When I fell sick with pining we didn't wait any more,
But moved away from the cornlands out to this river
shore—
The Tuscarawas it's called, sir—off there's a hill, you see—
And now I've grown to like it next best to the Tennessee.

I was at work that morning. Someone came riding like
mad
Over the bridge and up the road—Farmer Rouf's little
lad.
Bareback he rode; he had no hat; he hardly stopped to
say,
"Morgan's men are coming, Frau, they're galloping on this
way.

"I'm sent to warn the neighbors. He isn't a mile behind;
He sweeps up all the horses—every horse that he can find;
Morgan, Morgan the raider, and Morgan's terrible men,
With bowie knives and pistols, are galloping up the glen."

The lad rode down the valley, and I stood still at the
    door—
The baby laughed and prattled, playing with spools on the
    floor;
Kentuck was out in the pasture; Conrad, my man, was
    gone;
Near, near Morgan's men were galloping, galloping on!

Sudden I picked up baby and ran to the pasture bar:
"Kentuck!" I called; "Kentucky!" She knew me ever so far!
I led her down the gully that turns off there to the right,
And tied her to the bushes; her head was just out of sight.

As I ran back to the log house at once there came a
    sound—
The ring of hoofs, galloping hoofs, trembling over the
    ground,
Coming into the turnpike out from the White-Woman
    Glen—
Morgan, Morgan the raider, and Morgan's terrible men.

As near they drew and nearer my heart beat fast in alarm;
But still I stood in the doorway, with baby on my arm.
They came; they passed; with spur and whip in haste they
    sped along;
Morgan, Morgan the raider, and his band six hundred
    strong.

Weary they looked and jaded, riding through night and
    through day;

Pushing on east to the river, many long miles away,
To the border strip where Virginia runs up into the west,
And for the Upper Ohio before they could stop to rest.

On like the wind they hurried, and Morgan rode in
        advance;
Bright were his eyes like live coals, as he gave me a side-
        ways glance;
And I was just breathing freely, after my choking pain,
When the last one of the troopers suddenly drew his rein.

Frightened I was to death, sir; I scarce dared look in his
        face,
As he asked for a drink of water and glanced around the
        place;
I gave him a cup, and he smiled—'twas only a boy, you
        see,
Faint and worn, with his blue eyes; and he'd sailed on the
        Tennessee.

Only sixteen he was, sir—a fond mother's only son—
Off and away with Morgan before his life had begun!
The damp drops stood on his temples; drawn was the boy-
        ish mouth;
And I thought me of the mother waiting down in the
        South!

O, plucky was he to the backbone and clear grit through
        and through;
Boasted and bragged like a trooper; but the big words
        wouldn't do;
The boy was dying, sir, dying, as plain as plain could be,
Worn out by his ride with Morgan up from the Tennessee.

But, when I told the laddie that I too was from the South,
Water came in his dim eyes and quivers around his mouth.

"Do you know the Bluegrass country?" he wistful began to
    say,
Then swayed like a willow sapling and fainted dead away.

I had him into the log house, and worked and brought him
    to;
I fed him and coaxed him, as I thought his mother'd do;
And, when the lad got better, and the noise in his head
    was gone,
Morgan's men were miles away, galloping, galloping on.

"O, I must go," he muttered; "I must be up and away!
Morgan, Morgan is waiting for me! O, what will Morgan
    say?"
But I heard a sound of tramping and kept him back from
    the door—
The ringing sound of horses' hoofs that I had heard before.

And on, on came the soldiers—the Michigan cavalry—
And fast they rode, and black they looked galloping
    rapidly;
They had followed hard on Morgan's track; they had
    followed day and night;
But of Morgan and Morgan's raiders they had never
    caught a sight.

And rich Ohio sat startled through all those summer days,
For strange, wild men were galloping over her broad
    highways;
Now here, now there, now seen, now gone, now north,
    now east, now west,
Through river valleys and corn-land farms, sweeping away
    her best.

A bold ride and a long ride! But they were taken at last.
They almost reached the river by galloping hard and fast;

But the boys in blue were upon them ere ever they gained
    the ford,
And Morgan, Morgan the raider, laid down his terrible
    sword.

Well, I kept the boy till evening—kept him against his
    will—
But he was too weak to follow, and sat there pale and still;
When it was cool and dusky—you'll wonder to hear me
    tell—
But I stole down to that gully and brought up Kentucky
    Belle.

I kissed the star on her forehead—my pretty, gentle lass—
But I knew that she'd be happy back in the old Bluegrass;
A suit of clothes of Conrad's, with all the money I had,
And Kentuck, pretty Kentuck, I gave to the worn-out lad.

I guided him to the southward as well as I knew how;
The boy rode off with many thanks, and many a backward
    bow;
And then the glow it faded, and my heart began to swell,
As down the glen away she went, my lost Kentucky Belle!

When Conrad came in the evening the moon was shining
    high;
Baby and I were both crying—I couldn't tell him why—
But a battered suit of rebel gray was hanging on the wall,
And a thin old horse with drooping head stood in Ken-
    tucky's stall.

Well, he was kind, and never once said a hard word to me;
He knew I couldn't help it—'twas all for the Tennessee;
But, after the war was over, just think what came to
    pass—
A letter, sir; and the two were safe back in the old Blue-
    grass.

The lad had got across the border, riding Kentucky
    Belle;
And Kentuck she was thriving, and fat, and hearty, and
    well;
He cared for her, and kept her, nor touched her with whip
    or spur:
Ah! we've had many horses, but never a horse like her!

Constance Fenimore Woolson

ABDULLAH BULBUL AMIR

The sons of the Prophet are valiant and bold,
    And quite unaccustomed to fear;
And the bravest of all was a man, so I'm told,
    Called Abdullah Bulbul Amir.

When they wanted a man to encourage the van,
    Or harass the foe from the rear,
Storm fort or redoubt, they were sure to call out
    For Abdullah Bulbul Amir.

There are heroes in plenty, and well known to fame,
    In the legions that fight for the Czar;
But none of such fame as the man by the name
    Of Ivan Petrofsky Skovar.

He could imitate Irving, tell fortunes by cards,
    And play on the Spanish guitar;
In fact, quite the cream of the Muscovite guards
    Was Ivan Petrofsky Skovar.

One day this bold Muscovite shouldered his gun,
    Put on his most cynical sneer,
And was walking downtown when he happened to run
    Into Abdullah Bulbul Amir.

"Young man," said Bulbul, "is existence so dull
   That you're anxious to end your career?
Then, infidel, know you have trod on the toe
   Of Abdullah Bulbul Amir.

"So take your last look at the sea, sky and brook,
   Make your latest report on the war;
For I mean to imply you are going to die,
   O Ivan Petrofsky Skovar."

So this fierce man he took his trusty chibouk,
   And murmuring, "Allah Akbar!"
With murder intent he most savagely went
   For Ivan Petrofsky Skovar.

The Sultan rose up, the disturbance to quell,
   Likewise, give the victor a cheer.
He arrived just in time to bid hasty farewell
   To Abdullah Bulbul Amir.

A loud-sounding splash from the Danube was heard
   Resounding o'er meadows afar;
It came from the sack fitting close to the back
   Of Ivan Petrofsky Skovar.

There lieth a stone where the Danube doth roll,
   And on it in characters queer
Are "Stranger, when passing by, pray for the soul
   Of Abdullah Bulbul Amir."

A Muscovite maiden her lone vigil keeps
   By the light of the pale northern star,
And the name that she murmurs so oft as she weeps
   Is Ivan Petrofsky Skovar.

American song

BECAUSE I WERE SHY

As I were a-walking upon a fine day,
  I met a fine lady from over the way;
She smiled as she passed with a glint in her eye—
  But I stood and I bloosh-ed because I were shy.

Says I to meself, "Come, Johnny," says I,
  "If tha'd wish for to win her there's naught but to try."
So I doff-ed me 'at as I wink-ed me eye;
  Then I donn-ed it on again 'cause I were shy.

She walk-ed before me for nearly a mile
  Until she got stuck on the top of a stile.
Says she, "Willya 'elp me?" "I'll try it," says I;
  But I 'ollered for mother because I were shy.

She called me a noodle—I made a grimace,
  Then she lifted her fist and she slapp-ed me face,
When up came me brother so spruce and so spry
  And off I skedaddled because I were shy.

She 'ook-ed 'is arm, and she 'ook-ed 'im too;
  They were wedded as soon as the banns 'ad gone
    through.
Now they've lots of wee childer and troubles foreby—
  So I think I were lucky because I were shy.

English folk song

THE EDDYSTONE LIGHT

Me father was the keeper of the Eddystone Light,
He married a mer-my-aid one night;
Out of the match came children three—
Two was fish and the other was me.

> *Chorus:* Jolly stories, jolly told
> When the winds is bleak and the nights is cold;
> No such life can be led on the shore
> As is had on the rocks by the ocean's roar.

When I was but a boyish chip,
They put me in charge of the old lightship;
I trimmed the lamps and I filled 'em with oil,
And I played seven-up accordin' to Hoyle.

> *Chorus:* Jolly stories, jolly told
> When the winds is bleak and the nights is cold;
> No such life can be led on the shore
> As is had on the rocks by the ocean's roar.

One evenin' as I was a-trimmin' the glim
An' singin' a verse of the evenin' hymn,
I see by the light of me binnacle lamp
Me kind old father lookin' jolly and damp;
An' a voice from the starboard shouted "Ahoy!"
An' there was me gran'mother sittin' on a buoy—
Meanin' a buoy for ships what sail
An' not a boy what's a juvenile male.

> *Chorus:* Jolly stories, jolly told
> When the winds is bleak and the nights is cold;
> No such life can be led on the shore
> As is had on the rocks by the ocean's roar.

English folk song

THE FOX

The fox went out on a chilly night,
Prayed to the moon for to give him light,
For he'd many a mile to go that night
    Afore he reached the town-o.

He ran till he came to a great big bin;
The ducks and the geese were put therein.
"A couple of you will grease my chin,
    Afore I leave this town-o."

He grabbed the gray goose by the neck,
Throwed a duck across his back;
He didn't mind the "quack, quack, quack"
    And the legs a-dangling down-o.

Then old mother Flipper-Flopper jumped out of bed,
Out of the window she stuck her head,
Crying, "John! John! The gray goose is gone
    And the fox is on the town-o!"

Then John, he went to the top of the hill,
Blowed his horn both loud and shrill;
The fox, he said, "I better flee with my kill
    Or they'll soon be on my trail-o."

He ran till he came to his cozy den,
There were the little ones eight, nine, ten.
They said, "Daddy, better go back again,
    'Cause it must be a mighty fine town-o."

Then the fox and his wife without any strife,
Cut up the goose with a fork and knife;
They never had such a supper in their life
    And the little ones chewed on the bones-o."

Old ballad

GET UP AND BAR THE DOOR

It fell about the Martinmas time,
    And a gay time it was then,
When our goodwife got puddings to make,
    And she's boiled them in the pan.

The wind so cold blew south and north,
    And blew into the floor;
Quoth our goodman to our goodwife,
    "Get up and bar the door."

"My hand is in my household work,
    Goodman, as ye may see;
And it will not be barred for a hundred years,
    If it's to be barred by me!"

They made a pact between them both,
  They made it firm and sure,
That whosoe'er should speak the first,
  Should rise and bar the door.

Then by there came two gentlemen,
  At twelve o'clock at night,
And they could see neither house nor hall,
  Nor coal nor candlelight.

"Now whether is this a rich man's house,
  Or whether is it a poor?"
But never a word would one of them speak,
  For barring of the door

The guests they ate the white puddings,
  And then they ate the black;
Tho' much the goodwife thought to herself,
  Yet never a word she spake.

Then said one stranger to the other,
  "Here, man, take ye my knife;
Do ye take off the old man's beard,
  And I'll kiss the goodwife."

"There's no hot water to scrape it off,
  And what shall we do then?"
"Then why not use the pudding broth,
  That boils into the pan?"

O up then started our goodman,
  An angry man was he;
"Will ye kiss my wife before my eyes!
  And with pudding broth scald me!"

Then up and started our goodwife,
  Gave three skips on the floor:
"Goodman, you've spoken the foremost word.
  Get up and bar the door!"

Old ballad

GREEN BROOM

There was an old man lived out in the wood,
  His trade was a-cutting of Broom, green Broom;
He had but one son without thrift, without good,
  Who lay in his bed till 'twas noon, bright noon.

The old man awoke, one morning and spoke,
  He swore he would fire the room, that room,
If his John would not rise and open his eyes,
  And away to the wood to cut Broom, green Broom,

So Johnny arose, and he slipped on his clothes,
  And away to the wood to cut Broom, green Broom,
He sharpened his knives, for once he contrives
  To cut a great bundle of Broom, green Broom.

When Johnny passed under a lady's fine house,
  Passed under a lady's fine room, fine room,
She called to her maid, "Go fetch me," she said,
  "Go fetch me the boy that sells Broom, green Broom."

When Johnny came in to the lady's fine house,
  And stood in the lady's fine room, fine room;
"Young Johnny," she said, "will you give up your trade,
  And marry a lady in bloom, full bloom?"

Johnny gave his consent, and to church they both went,
   And he wedded the lady in bloom, full bloom,
At market and fair, all folks do declare,
   There is none like the Boy that sold Broom, green
      Broom.

Unknown

HOW ROBIN HOOD RESCUED THE WIDOW'S SONS

There are twelve months in all the year,
   As I hear many say,
But the merriest month in all the year
   Is the merry month of May.

Now Robin Hood is to Nottingham gone,
   With a link a down, and a day,
And there he met a silly old woman,
   Was weeping on the way.

"What news? what news? thou silly old woman,
   What news hast thou for me?"
Said she, "There's my three sons in Nottingham town
   To-day condemned to die."

"O, have they parishes burnt?" he said,
   "Or have they ministers slain?
Or have they robbed any virgin?
   Or other men's wives have ta'en?"

"They have no parishes burnt, good sir,
   Nor yet have ministers slain,
Nor have they robbed any virgin,
   Nor other men's wives have ta'en."

[225]

"O, what have they done?" said Robin Hood,
  "I pray thee tell to me."
"It's for slaying of the king's fallow-deer,
  Bearing their long bows with thee."

"Dost thou not mind, old woman," he said,
  "How thou mad'st me to sup and dine?
By the truth of my body," quoth bold Robin Hood,
  "You could not tell it in better time."

Now Robin Hood is to Nottingham gone,
  With a link a down, and a day,
And there he met with a silly old palmer,
  Was walking along the highway.

"What news? what news? thou silly old man,
  What news, I do thee pray?"
Said he, "Three squires in Nottingham town
  Are condemned to die this day."

"Come change thy apparel with me, old man,
  Come change thy apparel for mine;
Here is ten shillings in good silver,
  Go drink it in beer or wine."

"O, thine apparel is good," he said,
  "And mine is ragged and torn;
Wherever you go, wherever you ride,
  Laugh not an old man to scorn."

"Come change thy apparel with me, old churl,
  Come change thy apparel with mine;
Here is a piece of good broad gold,
  Go feast thy brethren with wine."

Then he put on the old man's hat,
   It stood full high on the crown:
"The first bold bargain that I come at,
   It shall make thee come down!"

Then he put on the old man's cloak,
   Was patched black, blue, and red;
He thought it no shame, all the day long,
   To wear the bags of bread.

Then he put on the old man's breeks,
   Was patched from leg to side:
"By the truth of my body," bold Robin can say,
   "This man loved little pride!"

Then he put on the old man's hose,
   Were patched from knee to wrist:
"By the truth of my body," said bold Robin Hood,
   "I'd laugh if I had any list."

Then he put on the old man's shoes,
   Were patched both beneath and aboon:
Then Robin Hood swore a solemn oath,
   "It's good habit that makes a man."

Now Robin Hood is to Nottingham gone,
   With a link a down, and a down,
And there he met with the proud sheriff,
   Was walking along the town.

"Save you, save you, sheriff!" he said;
   "Now heaven you save and see!
And what will you give to a silly old man
   To-day will your hangman be?"

"Some suits, some suits," the sheriff he said,
  "Some suits I'll give to thee;
Some suits, some suits, and pence thirteen,
  To-day's a hangman's fee."

Then Robin he turns him round about,
  And jumps from stock to stone:
"By the truth of my body," the sheriff he said,
  "That's well jumpt, thou nimble old man!"

"I was ne'er a hangman in all my life,
  Nor yet intends to trade:
But curst he be," said bold Robin,
  "That first was a hangman made!

"I've a bag for meal, and a bag for malt,
  And a bag for barley and corn;
A bag for bread, and a bag for beef,
  And a bag for my little small horn.

"I have a horn in my pocket,
   I got it from Robin Hood,
And still when I set it to my mouth,
   For thee it blows little good."

"O, wind thy horn, thou proud fellow!
   Of thee I have no doubt.
I wish that thou give such a blast,
   Till both thy eyes fall out."

The first loud blast that he did blow,
   He blew both loud and shrill;
A hundred and fifty of Robin Hood's men
   Came riding over the hill.

The next loud blast that he did give,
   He blew both loud and amain,
And quickly sixty of Robin Hood's men
   Came shining over the plain.

"O, who are those," the sheriff he said,
    "Come tripping over the lea?"
"They're my attendants," brave Robin did say;
    "They'll pay a visit to thee."

They took the gallows from the slack,
    They set it in the glen,
They hanged the proud sheriff on that,
    And released their own three men.

Old English ballad

KITTY OF COLERAINE

As beautiful Kitty one morning was tripping
    With a pitcher of milk for the fair of Coleraine,
When she saw me she stumbled, the pitcher down
        tumbled,
    And all the sweet buttermilk watered the plain.
"Oh, what shall I do now? 'Twas looking at you now!
    I'm sure such a pitcher I'll ne'er see again.
'Twas the pride of my dairy. Oh, Barney McCleary,
    You're sent as a plague to the girls of Coleraine."

I sat down beside her, and gently did chide her
    That such a misfortune should give her such pain;
A kiss then I gave her, and before I did leave her
    She vowed for such pleasure she'd break it again.
'Twas the haymaking season—I can't tell the reason—
    Misfortunes will never come single, 'tis plain!
For very soon after poor Kitty's disaster
    The devil a pitcher was whole in Coleraine.

Irish folk song

A LONGFORD LEGEND

Oh! 'tis of a bold major a tale I'll relate,
Who possessed a fine house and a charming estate,
Who, when possible, always his pleasure would take
From morning till night in a boat on his lake.
So a steam-launch he bought from a neighboring peer,
And learnt how to start her, to stoke, and to steer;
But part of the craft he omitted to learn—
How to ease her, and to stop her, and back her astern.

Well, one lovely spring morn from the moorings they cast,
The furnace alight and the steam in full blast.
As they cruised through the lake, oh! what pleasure was
      theirs!
What congratulations! what swagger! what airs!
"Evening's come," says the major; "let's home for the night.
I'll pick up the mooring and make her all right;
Whilst you, my gay stoker, your wages to earn,
Just ease her, and stop her, and back her astern."

"Do what?" asked the stoker. "Why, stop her, of course!"
"Faith! it's aisier stopping a runaway horse!
Just try it yourself!" the field officer swore!
But that was no use,—they were nearly on shore!
He swore at himself, at the boat, and the crew;
He cursed at the funnel, the boiler, the screw,—
But in vain! He was forced from his mooring to turn,
Shouting, "Ease her, and stop her, and back her astern!"

It was clear that on shore they that night would not dine,
So they drank up the brandy, the whisky and wine;
They finished the stew and demolished the cake
As they steamed at full speed all the night round the lake.

Weeks passed; and with terror and famine oppressed,
One by one of that ill-fated crew sank to rest;
And grim death seized the major before he could learn
How to ease her, and stop her, and back her astern.

And still round the lake their wild course they pursue,
While the ghost of the major still swears at the crew,
And the ghosts of the crew still reply in this mode,
"Just ease her, and stop her yourself—and be blowed!"
Here's the moral: Imprimis, whene'er you're afloat,
Don't use haughty words to your crew on your boat;
And ere starting, oh! make this your deepest concern—
Learn to ease her, and stop her, and back her astern.

Irish ballad

MAY COLVIN

False Sir John a-wooing came,
　　To a maid of beauty rare;
May Colvin was the lady's name,
　　Her father's only heir.

He wooed her indoors, he wooed her out,
　　He wooed her night and day;
Until he got the lady's consent
　　To mount and ride away.

"Go fetch me some of your father's gold
　　And some of your mother's fee,
And I'll carry you to the far Northland
　　And there I'll marry thee."

She's gone to her father's coffers,
　　Where all his money lay;

And she's taken the red, and she's left the white,
   And lightly she's tripped away.

She's gone down to her father's stable,
   Where all his steeds did stand;
And she's taken the best and left the worst,
   That was in her father's land.

He rode on, and she rode on,
   They rode a long summer's day,
Until they came to a broad river,
   An arm of a lonesome sea.

"Leap off the steed," says false Sir John;
   "Your bridal bed you see;
For it's seven fair maids I have drownèd here,
   And the eighth one you shall be.

"Cast off, cast off your silks so fine,
   And lay them on a stone,
For they are too fine and costly
   To rot in the salt sea foam."

"O turn about, thou false Sir John,
   And look to the leaf o' the tree;
For it never became a gentleman
   A naked woman to see."

He's turned himself straight round about
   To look to the leaf o' the tree;
She's twined her arms about his waist,
   And thrown him into the sea.

"O hold a grip of me, May Colvin,
   For fear that I should drown;

I'll take you home to your father's gates,
  And safe I'll set you down."

"O safe enough I am, Sir John,
  And safer I will be;
For seven fair maids have you drownèd here,
  The eighth shall not be me.

"O lie you there, thou false Sir John,
  O lie you there," said she,
"For you lie not in a colder bed
  Than the one you intended for me."

So she went on her father's steed,
  As swift as she could away;
And she came home to her father's gates
  At the breaking of the day.

Up then spake the pretty parrot:
  "May Colvin, where have you been?
What has become of false Sir John,
  That wooed you yestere'en?"

"O hold your tongue, my pretty parrot,
  Nor tell no tales on me;
Your cage will be made of the beaten gold
  With spokes of ivory."

Up then spake her father dear,
  In the chamber where he lay:
"What ails you, pretty parrot,
  That you prattle so long ere day?"

"There came a cat to my door, master,
  I thought 'twould have worried me;
And I was calling on May Colvin
  To take the cat from me."

Old ballad

OLD WICHET

I went into my stable, to see what I might see,
And there I saw three horses stand, by one, by two, **by**
      three.
I called unto my loving wife, and "Coming Sir!" said she,
"O what do these three horses here without the leave **of**
      me?"
  "Why, old fool, blind fool! can't you very well see,
  That these are three milking cows my mother sent **to**
      me?"
"Hey boys! Fill the cup! Milking cows with saddles up!
The like was never known, the like was never known."
Old Wichet went a noodle out, a noodle he came home.

I went into the kitchen, to see what I might see,
And there I saw three swords hung up, by one, by two, **by**
      three.
I called unto my loving wife, and "Coming Sir!" said she,
"O why do these three swords hang here without the **leave**
      of me?"
  "Why, old fool, blind fool! can't you very well see,
  That these are three toasting-forks my mother sent **to**
      me?"

"Hey boys! Well done! Toasting-forks with scabbards on!
The like was never known, the like was never known."
Old Wichet went a noodle out, a noodle he came home.

I went into the pantry, to see what I might see,
And there I saw three pairs of boots, by one, by two, by
      three.
I called unto my loving wife, and "Coming Sir!" said she,
"O what do these three pairs of boots without the leave of
      me?"
    "Why, old fool, blind fool! can't you very well see,
    That these are three pudding-bags my mother sent to
      me?"
Hey boys! Well done! Pudding-bags with steel spurs on!
The like was never known, the like was never known."
Old Wichet went a noodle out, a noodle he came home.

I went into the dairy, to see what I might see,
And there I saw three beavers,* by one, by two, by three.
I called unto my loving wife, and "Coming Sir!" said she,
"O what do these three beavers here without the leave of
      me?"
    "Why, old fool, blind fool! can't you very well see,
    That these are three milking-pails my mother sent to
      me?"
"Hey boys! Well done! Milking-pails with ribbons on!
The like was never known, the like was never known."
Old Wichet went a noodle out, a noodle he came home.

I went into the chamber, to see what I might see,
And there I saw three men in bed, by one, by two, by
      three.
I called unto my loving wife, and "Coming Sir!" said she,
"O why sleep here three gentlemen without the leave of
      me?"

* Felt hats.

"Why, old fool, blind fool! can't you very well see,
    That these are three milking-maids my mother sent to
        me?"
"Hey boys! Well done! Milking-maids with beards on!
The like was never known, the like was never known."
Old Wichet went a noodle out, a noodle he came home.

I went into the chamber, as quick as quick might be,
I kicked the three men down the stairs, by one, by two, by
        three.
"Without your hats and boots be off, your horses leave and
        flee,
Your purses 'neath your pillows left; they too belong to me.
    Why, old wife, blind wife! can't you very well see,
    That these are three highwaymen from justice hid by
        thee?
"Hey boys! Purses left! Knaves they be, and away are
        flown.
The like was never known, the like was never known."
Old Wichet went a noodle out, a wise man he came home.

                                                    Old ballad

THE SAD TALE OF MR. MEARS

There was a man who had a clock,
    His name was Matthew Mears;
And every day he wound that clock
    For eight and twenty years.

And then one day he found that clock
    An eight-day clock to be,
And a madder man than Matthew Mears
    You would not wish to see.

                                                    Unknown

THE SNUFF-BOXES

A village pedagogue announced one day
Unto his pupils, that Inspector A.
Was coming to examine them.   Quoth he:
"If he should try you in Geography,
Most likely he will ask—'What's the Earth's shape?'
Then, if you feel as stupid as an ape,
Just look at me: my snuff-box I will show,
Which will remind you it is round, you know."

Now, the sagacious master, I declare,
Had two snuff-boxes—one round, t'other square;
The square he carried through the week, the round
On Sundays only.
                    Hark! a footstep's sound:
'Tis the Inspector.   "What's the Earth's shape, lad?"
Addressing one by name. The latter, glad
To have his memory helped, looked at the master;
When, piteous to relate, O, sad disaster!
The pupil without hesitation says:
"Round, sir, on Sundays, square on other days."

Unknown

THERE WAS AN OLD WOMAN

There was an old woman, as I've heard tell,
She went to the market, her eggs for to sell;
She went to market all on a market-day.
And she fell asleep on the king's highway.

There came by a pedlar whose name was Stout;
He cut her petticoats all round about;
He cut her petticoats up to the knees,
Which made the old woman to shiver and freeze.

When this little woman did first wake,
She began to shiver and she began to shake;
She began to wonder and she began to cry,
"Oh! deary, deary me, this is none of I!

"But if it be I, as I do hope it be,
I've a little dog at home, and he'll know me;
If it be I, he'll wag his little tail,
And if it be not I, he'll loudly bark and wail."

Home went the little woman all in the dark;
Up got the little dog and he began to bark;
He began to bark, so she began to cry,
"Oh! deary, deary me, this is none of I!"

Unknown

TRUE THOMAS

True Thomas lay on Huntlie bank;
    A marvel he did see;
For there he saw a lady bright,
    Come riding down by the Eildon tree.

Her skirt was of the grass-green silk,
    Her mantle of the velvet fine;
On every lock of her horse's mane,
    Hung fifty silver bells and nine.

True Thomas he pulled off his cap,
  And bowed low down on his knee;
"All hail, thou mighty Queen of Heaven!
  For thy peer on earth could never be."

"O no, O no, Thomas," she said,
  "That name does not belong to me;
I'm but the Queen of fair Elfland,
  That hither am come to visit thee.

"Harp and carp, Thomas," she said,
  "Harp and carp along with me;
And if ye dare to kiss my lips,
  Sure of your body I will be!"

"Betide me weal, betide me woe,
  That threat shall never frighten me!"
Then he has kissed her on the lips,
  All underneath the Eildon tree.

"Now ye must go with me," she said,
  "True Thomas, ye must go with me;
And ye must serve me seven years,
  Through weal or woe as may chance to be."

She's mounted on her milk-white steed,
  She's taken True Thomas up behind;
And aye, whene'er her bridle rang,
  The steed flew swifter than the wind.

O they rode on, and farther on,
  The steed flew swifter than the wind;
Until they reached a desert wide,
  And living land was left behind.

"Light down, light down now, Thomas," she said,
"And lean your head upon my knee;
Light down, and rest a little space,
And I will show you marvels three.

"O see ye not yon narrow road,
So thick beset with thorns and briers?
That is the path of righteousness,
Though after it but few enquires.

"And see ye not yon broad, broad road,
That stretches o'er the lily leven?
That is the path of wickedness,
Though some call it the road to heaven.

"And see ye not yon bonny road,
That winds about the green hillside?
That is the way to fair Elfland,
Where you and I this night must bide.

"But, Thomas, ye shall hold your tongue,
Whatever ye may hear or see;
For if ye speak word in Elfin land,
Ye'll ne'er win back to your own countree!"

O they rode on, and farther on;
They waded through rivers above the knee,
And they saw neither sun nor moon,
But they heard the roaring of a sea.

It was mirk, mirk night; there was no star-light;
They waded through red blood to the knee;
For all the blood that's shed on earth,
Runs through the springs o' that countree.

At last they came to a garden green,
　　And she pulled an apple from on high—
"Take this for thy wages, True Thomas;
　　It will give thee the tongue that can never lie!"

"My tongue is my own," True Thomas he said,
　　"A goodly gift ye would give to me!
I neither could to buy or sell
　　At fair or tryst where I may be.

"I could neither speak to prince or peer,
　　Nor ask of grace from fair ladye."
"Now hold thy peace!" the lady said,
　　"For as I say, so must it be."

He has gotten a coat of the even cloth,
　　And a pair of shoes of the velvet green;
And till seven years were gone and past,
　　True Thomas on earth was never seen.

Old ballad

THE TWA CORBIES

As I was walking all alane
I heard twa corbies* making a mane;
The tane unto the t'other say,
"Where sall we gang and dine to-day?

"—In behint yon auld fail dyke
I wot there lies a new-slain knight;
And naebody kens that he lies there,
But his hawk, and hound, and lady fair.

* Two ravens.

[242]

"His hound is to the hunting gane,
His hawk to fetch the wild-fowl hame,
His lady's ta'en another mate,
So we may mak our dinner sweet.

"Ye'll sit on his white hause-bane,
And I'll pick out his bonnie blue een:
Wi' ae lock o' his gowden hair
We'll theek our nest when it grows bare.

"Mony a one for him makes mane,
But nane sall ken where he is gane;
O'er his white banes, when they are bare,
The wind sall blaw for evermair."

Old Scottish ballad

WALTZING MATILDA

Once a jolly swagman camped by a billabong*
Under the shade of a coolibah tree.
And he sang as he watched and waited till his billy boiled:
"You'll come a-waltzing, Matilda, with me!"

Chorus:
Waltzing, Matilda, waltzing, Matilda,
You'll come a-waltzing, Matilda, with me.
And he sang as he watched and waited till his billy boiled,
"You'll come a-waltzing, Matilda, with me!"

Down came a jumbuck† to drink at the billabong,
Up jumped the swagman and grabbed him with glee,
And he sang as he stowed that jumbuck in his tucker bag:
"You'll come a-waltzing, Matilda, with me!"

* mudhole
† sheep

Chorus:
Waltzing, Matilda, waltzing, Matilda,
You'll come a-waltzing, Matilda, with me.
And he sang as he stowed that jumbuck in his tucker bag:
"You'll come a-waltzing, Matilda, with me!"

Up rode the squatter mounted on his thoroughbred,
Down came the troopers, one, two, three,
And his, "Where's that jolly jumbuck you've got in your
        tucker bag?"
"You'll come a-waltzing, Matilda, with me!"

Chorus:
Waltzing, Matilda, waltzing, Matilda,
You'll come a-waltzing, Matilda, with me.
And his, "Where's that jolly jumbuck you've got in your
        tucker bag?"
"You'll come a-waltzing, Matilda, with me!"

Up jumped the swagman, sprang into the billabong.
"You'll never catch me alive," said he.
And his ghost may be heard as you pass by that billabong:
"You'll come a-waltzing, Matilda, with me!"

Chorus:
Waltzing, Matilda, waltzing, Matilda,
You'll come a-waltzing, Matilda, with me.
And his ghost may be heard as you pass by that billabong:
"You'll come a-waltzing, Matilda, with me!"

Australian folk song

[245]

THE ZEBRA DUN

We were camped on the plains at the head of the Cimarron
When along came a stranger and stopped to arger some,
He seemed so very foolish that we began to look around,
We thought he was a greenhorn that had just 'scaped from
      town.

We asked if he'd been to breakfast; he hadn't had a smear,
So we opened up the chuck-box and bade him have his
      share.
He took a cup of coffee and some biscuits and some beans,
And then began to talk and tell about foreign kings and
      queens,—

About the Spanish war and the fighting on the seas
With guns as big as steers and ramrods big as trees,—
And about Old Paul Jones, a mean, fighting son of a gun,
Who was the grittiest cuss that ever pulled a gun.

Such an educated feller, his thoughts just came in herds,
He astonished all them cowboys with them jaw-breaking
      words.
He just kept on talking till he made the boys all sick,
And they began to look around just how to play a trick.

He said that he had lost his job upon the Santa Fé
And was going across the plains to strike the 7-D.
He didn't say how come it, some trouble with the boss,
But said he'd like to borrow a nice fat saddle hoss.

This tickled all the boys to death, they laughed down in
      their sleeves,—
"We'll lend you a horse just as fresh and fat as you please."

Shorty grabbed a lariat and roped the Zebra Dun,
Turned him over to the stranger and waited for the fun.

Old Dunny was a rocky outlaw that had grown so awful
    wild
That he could paw the white out of the moon every jump
    for a mile.
Old Dunny stood right still,—as if he didn't know,—
Until he was saddled and ready for to go.

When the stranger hit the saddle, old Dunny quit the
    earth
And traveled right straight up for all that he was worth.
A-pitching and a-squealing, a-having wall-eyed fits,
His hind feet perpendicular, his front ones in the bits.

We could see the tops of the mountains under Dunny every
    jump,
But the stranger he was growed there just like the camel's
    hump;
The stranger sat upon him and curled his black mustache
Just like a summer boarder waiting for his hash.

He thumped him in the shoulders and spurred him when
    he whirled,
To show them flunky punchers that he was the wolf of the
    world.
When the stranger had dismounted once more upon the
    ground,
We knew he was a thoroughbred and not a gent from
    town.

The boss who was standing round, a-watching of the show,
Walked right up to the stranger and told him he needn't
    go,—

"If you can use the lasso like you rode old Zebra Dun,
You're the man I've been looking for ever since the year
      of one."

Oh, he could twirl the lariat and he didn't do it slow,
He could catch them forefeet nine out of ten for any kind
      of dough.
And when the herd stampeded he was always on the spot
And set them to nothing, like the boiling of a pot.

There's one thing and a shore thing I've learned since I've
      been born,
That every educated feller ain't a plumb greenhorn.

American cowboy ballad

TITLE INDEX

Abdullah Bulbul Amir   216
Allen-a-Dale   170
Annabel Lee   156
Arrogant Frog and the Superior Bull, The   37

Ballad of the Harp-weaver, The   140
Ballad of the Little Black Hound   178
Baucis and Philemon   189
Because I Were Shy   219
Bishop Hatto   183
Blacksmith's Serenade, The   118
Blind Men and the Elephant, The   163
Blow Me Eyes!   98
Boy Who Laughed at Santa Claus, The   146
Brady's Bend   107
Brown's Descent   60

Cape Horn Gospel—I   137
Casey at the Bat   197
Caulker, The   115
Christmas at Sea   187
Cremation of Sam McGee, The   173

Deacon's Masterpiece, The   86
Death of Robin Hood, The   51
Dog's Cold Nose, The   76
Dream of Eugene Aram, The   91

Eddystone Light, The   220
Embarrassing Episode of Little Miss Muffet, The   38

Fall of J. W. Beane, The   82
Figure-head, The   64
Finnigin to Flannigan   75

Flannan Isle   66
flattered lightning bug, the   134
Forty Singing Seamen   148
Fox, The   221

Get Up and Bar the Door   222
Glory Trail, The   40
Grandfather Watts's Private Fourth   35
Green Broom   224
Green Fiddler, The   54
Green Gnome, The   33

Henry VIII   50
Highwayman's Ghost, The   63
How Robin Hood Rescued the Widow's Sons   225

In Hardin County, 1809   200

Jesse James   29

Kentucky Belle   209
Kitty of Coleraine   230
Knight's Leap, The   110

La Belle Dame Sans Merci   105
Lady Clare   194
Lady Comes to an Inn, A   42
Legend of Lake Okeefinokee, A   158
Lochinvar   171
Longford Legend, A   231
Lord Arnaldos   59
Luck of Edenhall, The   120

Matilda   21
May Colvin   232
Molly Means   202
Mountain Whippoorwill, The   23

Nautical Extravaganza, A   100

Off the Ground   46
Old Man and Jim, The   160

Old Navy, The   135
Old Wichet   235
Owl-critic, The   56

Paddy O'Rafther   128
Paul Revere's Ride   122
Perils of Invisibility, The   71
Powerful Eyes o' Jeremy Tait, The   102
Priest and the Mulberry Tree, The   154
Princess and the Gypsies, The   43

Relief of Lucknow, The   129
Richard Cory   162

Sad Tale of Mr. Mears, The   237
Sheep   45
Skipper Ireson's Ride   205
small talk   133
Snuff-boxes, The   238
Song of the All-wool Shirt   53
Spelling Bee at Angels, The   78
Spinning Wheel, The   204
Story of Samuel Jackson, The   112

There Lived a King   70
There Was an Old Woman   238
Three Songs, The   193
True Thomas   239
Twa Corbies, The   242

Waltzing Matilda   243
War-song of Dinas Vawr, The   155

Yarn of the Loch Achray, The   138
Youth and the Northwind, The   165

Zebra Dun, The   246

INDEX OF FIRST LINES

a lightning bug got   134
A strong imagination from my youth has been
    combined   115
A village pedagogue announced one day   238
Across the seas of Wonderland to Mogadore we
    plodded,   148
Allen-a-Dale has no fagot for burning,   170
An old sea-dog on a sailor's log   102
As beautiful Kitty one morning was tripping   230
As I came over the humpbacked hill   54
As I looked out one May morning   43
As I was walking all alane   242
As I were a-walking upon a fine day,   219

Bluff King Hal was full of beans;   50
Brown lived at such a lofty farm   60

Did you hear of the curate who mounted his mare,   154

False Sir John a-wooing came,   232

"Give me my bow," said Robin Hood,   51
Grandfather Watts used to tell us boys   35

Have you heard of the wonderful one-hoss shay,   86

I stood one day by the breezy bay   100
"I was in a hooker once," said Karlssen,   137
I went into my stable, to see what I might see,   235
i went into the flea circus   133
I'll tell you of a sailor now, a tale that can't be beat,   112
In all the Eastern hemisphere   82
In ancient times, as story tells,   189

In Baltimore there lived a boy.   146
It fell about the Martinmas time,   222
It looked extremely rocky for the Mudville nine
    that day;   197
It was many and many a year ago,   156
It was six men of Indostan,   163
It was the time when lilies blow   194

Jesse James was a two-gun man,   29
John Littlehouse the redhead was a large ruddy man   118

King Siegfried sat in his lofty hall: 193

Listen, my children, and you shall hear   122
Little Miss Muffet discovered a tuffet,   38

Matilda told such Dreadful Lies,   21
Me father was the keeper of the Eddystone Light,   220
Mellow the moonlight to shine is beginning,   204
My father bought an undershirt   53

O what can ail thee, knight-at-arms,   105
O, young Lochinvar is come out of the west,   171
Of all the rides since the birth of time,   205
Of Edenhall, the youthful Lord   120
Oh, that last day in Lucknow fort!   129
Oh! 'tis of a bold major a tale I'll relate,   231
Old man never had much to say—   160
Old Molly Means was a hag and a witch;   202
Old PETER led a wretched life—   71
Once a jolly swagman camped by a billabong   243
Once, on a time and in a place   37
Once on a time—'twas long ago—   165

Paddy, in want of a dinner one day,   128

Ring, sing! ring, sing! pleasant Sabbath bells!   33

So the foemen have fired the gate, men of mine;   110
"Son," said my mother,   140
Summer of 'sixty-three, sir, and Conrad was gone
    away—   209
Superintindint was Flannigan;   75

The captain stood on the carronade: "First lieutenant," says he, 135

The fox went out on a chilly night, 221

The *Loch Achray* was a clipper tall 138

The mountain sheep are sweeter, 155

The sheets were frozen hard, and they cut the naked hand; 187

The sons of the Prophet are valiant and bold, 216

The strangest of adventures, 59

The summer and autumn had been so wet 183

There are strange things done in the midnight sun 173

There are twelve months in all the year, 225

There lived a King, as I've been told, 70

There once was a frog, 158

There was a man who had a clock, 237

There was an ancient carver that carved of a saint, 64

There was an old man lived out in the wood, 224

There was an old woman, as I've heard tell, 238

This is the story of 107

"Though three men dwell on Flannan Isle 66

Three jolly Farmers 46

Three strange men came to the inn, 42

True Thomas lay on Huntlie bank; 239

'Twas in the prime of summer time, 91

Twelve o'clock—a misty night— 63

Up in the mountains, it's lonesome all the time, 23

Waltz in, waltz in, ye little kids, and gather round my knee, 78

'Way high up the Mogollons, 40

We were camped on the plains at the head of the Cimarron 246

When I was once in Baltimore, 45

When I was young and full o' pride, 98

When Noah, perceiving 'twas time to embark, 76

When Richard Cory went down town, 162

Who knocks at the Geraldine's door to-night 178

"Who stuffed that white owl?" No one spoke in the shop: 56

With flintlocked guns and polished stocks, 200

DATE DUE			
MAR 23	JUN 1 '69		
APR 7	Conway		
SEP 30			
OCT 1 8			
FEB 5 '81			
OCT 27			
Conway			

Cole 1119